RARE COURAGE

Standing For Right When You Are Surrounded By Wrong

Jodi O'Malley, MSN, RN

Rare Courage
© 2022 Jodi O' Malley, MSN, RN

All scripture quotations, unless otherwise noted, are taken from the New King James Version (NKJV).

Printed in the United States of America

ISBN: 13 979-8-9874808-0-9

DISCLAIMER: The information and advice presented in this book are meant to help inform the decisions you make with your healthcare provider (and for any decisions related to health care for anyone under your legal control—such as children, family members, etc.). It is not meant to substitute for the advice of any physician or other trained health care professionals. You are advised to consult with health care professionals with regard to all matters pertaining to your and your family's health and well-being.

Some of the names and personal characteristics of the patients discussed have been changed in order to disguise their identities. Any resulting resemblance to persons living or dead is entirely coincidental and unintentional.

Dedication

To Angel, this started with you.

Table of Contents

Foreword

In the setting of a crisis, the rarity of courage cannot be overstated. We have seen this throughout the SARS-CoV-2 pandemic. Compassion, critical thinking, and careful re-evaluation were thrown out the windows of hospitals as mass panic and government bribes ushered in nihilistic protocols and horrific new standards of care resulting in deadly outcomes for patients who were denied early home treatment and found themselves hospitalized with COVID-19.

Jodi O'Malley is a mother, nurse, heroine, and patriot who would not stand by and let SARS-CoV-2 slaughter her patients. She set out to tell the world what really happened inside of hospitals in this gripping account of her nursing career during the pandemic. With the strength of a lioness, she risked it all and paid the professional price for blowing the whistle on wrongdoing and exposing the corruption, lies, and malfeasance within hospital and nursing administrations.

In this masterful work of nonfiction, O'Malley tells the world the truth when millions of nurses are complicit or too frightened to stand up for their patients to this day. We can all take heart in the odyssey of Jodi O'Malley and the rare courage she displayed while standing for right when she was surrounded by wrong.

Dr. Peter A. McCullough, MD, MPH

During the COVID pandemic, all too few health professionals stood up against our misguided and destructive public health policies. Jodi O'Malley was among the rare exceptions. She is a nurse who courageously risked her career to put her patient's first, suffering retaliation from a corrupt healthcare institution. Had there been one hundred other nurses like her in this country, the worst excesses and harms of our misguided COVID policies may have been averted. Read this book to be inspired by a woman of true integrity and fortitude.

> Dr. Aaron Khierarty, MD
> Chief of Psychiatry & Ethics at Doc1 Health
> Chief of Medical Ethics at The Unity Project

Jodi has risked her career and her livelihood to do what is right, even though doing what is right isn't always the most popular thing to do. In my opinion, the world needs more nurses like her.

> Kamaleilani Moreno, RN

It is said that having integrity requires courage to decide your actions and beliefs based on your morals rather than following the status quo of others. Jodi has always had integrity in her beliefs despite any potential backlash and has always had a courageous spirit, forging her own path even with high adversity. Her spirit and determination to always put the patient first is admirable especially in the light of the last few years when questioning the "normal" has been considered taboo. May we all find the courage that Jodi displays not only for our patients but for humanity.

> Racheal Hacke, ARNP
> Psychiatric Mental Health Nurse Practitioner

Chapter One

Something Isn't Right

I say it all the time, "I feel like I'm living in the Twilight Zone." Since February 2020, it's felt like I'm in a dream. Some moments are awe-inspiring, and others are like a form of hell.

It all started when word spread that a novel virus had originated in Wuhan, China, from the wet markets. The theory at the time was that patient zero had eaten bat soup, and the virus had jumped to humans. From all accounts, it was a respiratory virus that caused shortness of breath, extreme fatigue, muscle aches, loss of taste and smell, and seemingly affected the elderly far worse in terms of hospitalization and death. Children and parents would handle these symptoms like a cold.

When word of this new virus got around the nurses' station at the hospital, the common hypothesis was that we had already dealt with it in the 2019-2020 flu season (which runs from October 1st to May 1st, each year). During this time, many people were hit with the "worst flu ever." During those months, we saw a lot of respiratory illnesses of mysterious origin that, on the surface, produced flu-like symptoms. Every time the patient would test negative for the flu. Our discharge diagnosis would be: viral illness, pneumonia, or bronchitis, and the vast majority of patients were sent home with supportive therapy. Many of my coworkers had their own sickness stories during this time, and

I was no different.

I returned from visiting a friend in Seattle on Monday, February 19th. The next day, my daughter and her six-month-old baby came to spend time with me at my apartment. While I felt drained, I attributed that to jet lag and partying for three days prior to flying. Wednesday, they visited again, and I was in close contact with the little one. The usual grandmother stuff, hugging, kissing, cuddling, etc.

Around 1:00 PM that day, I went to lie down, and that was when the fever, fatigue, and muscle aches kicked in. The pain became so intense that I even struggled to get up to the bathroom. For three days, all I did was sleep and wither in bed from the intense muscle pain throughout my body. Every time I woke up drenched from sweat, I would take more vitamins, Tylenol, and Ibuprofen.

Even though my symptoms were severe, I never tested for the flu because you usually treat the symptoms, stay hydrated, and get over it with time and rest. If you catch it early, you can take Tamiflu, but it only shows to lessen symptoms by one day and comes with common side effects like diarrhea, nausea, or vomiting. As an ER nurse, when handing a patient this prescription, I always made sure to educate them because I know many do not take the time to read the side effect warnings.

On day two, I was so short of breath I slept sitting up. I often contemplated going to the hospital, but the fatigue was so severe, and I would drift off to sleep. My eldest son came to check on me and, with authority, said, "Mom, you've got to get up! Come on. I'll run you a bath and make you some tea."

It was all I could do to get out of bed. I remember thinking to myself, "If I can make it through this bath without struggling to breathe, I won't need to go to the hospital." Fortunately, I never did need to go there.

Saturday morning, the tiredness and muscle aches subsided. I hadn't had a fever in twenty-four hours, but I knew

I needed to get on an antibiotic and steroid, given my history of bronchitis. If I didn't already have pneumonia, I'd surely get it from three days of not moving. After calling the tele-doc and getting prescribed azithromycin, an antibiotic to kill any possible secondary infections, and methylprednisolone, a steroid to open up my airways, I began to feel better within a few hours of my first dose.

I returned to work at the hospital a day later, fever free for twenty-four hours. Of course, that has always been "protocol."

As a critical care nurse working in the hospital float pool, I often moved to various departments, filling in as needed. One night, I was working the medical-surgical floor, otherwise known as the med-surg. It was late, and we weren't too busy, so I was making small talk with another nurse about this new mystery virus.

"What do you think about this virus that's going around?" I asked.

"Crazy stuff, huh? I think it's been going around here for months. We just didn't know what it was."

"I think I had it," I told her.

"Really?"

"Yeah. I went to Seattle to visit a friend, and I was so sick a couple of days later. I had a fever, my entire body was in pain, and I was extremely tired. I could barely stay awake, let alone function. I was so short of breath with difficulty breathing."

She gasped, "That's where all the COVID cases come from! They're calling it "The Hotspot," and you just described all the classic symptoms. I bet that's what you had. My husband had it, too."

"Well, I probably did get it then," I responded. "But no one in my house has gotten sick except me."

"That's interesting."

"I mean, yeah. My apartment is really small, only 900 square feet. So we were all in close proximity. But I'm the only one who had symptoms. If I had COVID, though, wouldn't everyone else have gotten sick, too?"

The next night, I was floated to the intensive care unit, and the conversation about COVID came up again.

"What do you make of all this COVID stuff?" I asked a fellow nurse.

She talked in a hushed tone, so soft that no one else could hear, " I work as a flight nurse on the side when I'm not working here at the hospital," she whispered. "Back in December, I flew to China, roughly forty-five minutes from Wuhan, to pick up a sick patient and bring them back to the States for treatment. We ended up getting stuck there for two days because the patient was in too bad of shape to fly. They needed to get his platelet levels up before we could take him. On the way home, the pilot had to stop in Alaska for fuel, but he fell ill with flu-like symptoms and couldn't fly the rest of the way. Then, one of my crew members became sick with the same symptoms a day after arriving home."

"Oh my gosh, really?" I inquired, shocked at what I was hearing.

"Next thing I know, my husband is sick, and then my son. I never got it, though."

Immediately, I thought, "Who are we to kid ourselves that Seattle is the only place with this virus? If this chick was in Wuhan a couple of months ago on a flight mission, and it's as contagious as everybody is making it out to be, then it has to have already traveled the world!"

I wasn't worried about it. After all, I had all the symptoms, and I was around my entire family, and they were okay, so maybe this wasn't as bad as everybody was making it out to be. Looking back, I'd stayed in my room and kept my windows open and fans going in all the rooms, increasing ventilation and circulation. I wonder if that lowered the viral concentration of the virus (which we now know is airborne) and is why I got better so quickly. After all, this is one of the measures the

Industrial Hygiene Hierarchy of Controls states to take. I first learned this from Stephen Petty, the foremost Exposure Scientist in the country.

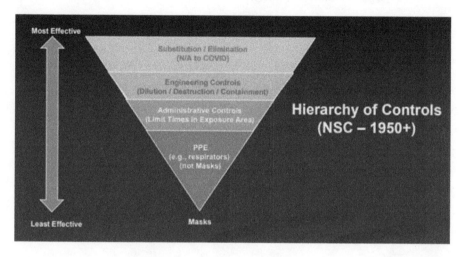

Courtesy of Stephen Petty

With the country and the rest of the world on mandatory lockdown to "stop the spread," most of us were glued to the daily press reports on television.

A number of talk show hosts and news reporters were all pondering whether Americans, like the Chinese, should begin wearing masks. This, along with widespread fear about the pandemic, caused everyday people to rush out and buy up all the gloves and masks that could be found. The rush for personal protective equipment (PPE) caused a shortage for healthcare providers.

Dr. Anthony Fauci showed up on the scene and told everybody not to wear a mask. He said that we weren't a "nation of mask wearers" and that they did nothing to stop the virus. Even the surgeon general spoke out against it.

His comment came out after the U.S. confirmed its second COVID-19 death, a person in Washington state. Then, on February 29th, 2020, the public freak-out began on Twitter over how safe and effective masks were.

"Seriously, people, masks? Are we going to have to start wearing hazmat suits next?" I thought to myself. Despite the growing panic that this was the deadliest virus in a hundred years, I hadn't heard any accounts of people dropping dead in the streets.

I remember being in the ER when I learned that flights were canceled. I literally looked up to the heavens and said to the Lord, "I'm supposed to pay attention to this, right?"

For the first time ever, this was a global concern. "Two weeks to slow the spread" was the phrase coined by every major news outlet, endorsing mass lockdowns to prevent the further spread of COVID-19. Washington's deaths began to slow down, as many of them were only from one nursing home. But then, New

York City started to get hit with cases. And just like that, there was a 24/7 death toll ticker on every TV, computer, and phone!

Tests were slowly being phased in. You could only get one if you were symptomatic (which is who these tests are intended for anyway) or if you had recently traveled to China. New York made a public statement, saying they needed nurses and ventilators because patients were dying at increasingly alarming rates. Yet, when I spoke with several nurses who lived in New York or went on a travel assignment there, they said their hospital was just as empty as mine.

"To all my fellow healthcare workers. First off, thank you for keeping your heart open, a smile on your face, and choosing to stay positive in the midst of this uncertainty. Thank you for showing up for your shift, even though we don't have the proper PPE, and for not making us work shorthanded. Thank you for being open to dialogue and listening without outward judgment. I appreciate and pray for all of us these days.

I've always questioned things that don't make sense. I do so relentlessly until it does. These days have been mentally exhausting. I need to take a step back, or maybe a mile, LOL, from constantly updating my feeds. In other words, significantly limit my screen time for my sanity and spirit. I just finished three twelve-hour shifts, one in the ER and one outside, where I was assessing for true emergencies or providing education guidance, and a third the night before in the ICU.

I'm curious to know what your hospital is like. What's the consensus on COVID-19? Are staff worried? How concerned are your patients about the virus or the state of our country? Have you seen a decline in people coming into the ER? How many people are testing negative for flu A and B but still have severe respiratory issues that can't be attributed to comorbidity and either tested positive for this virus or are awaiting results?

From my viewpoint, the majority of us aren't nearly as worried about this virus as we are for the fabric of our society. Many of us either know someone or have experienced flu-like shortness of breath in the last couple of months and can map out the transmission."

- Jodi O'Malley, Facebook, February 23rd, 2020

I had to be especially careful what I said and to whom during this time because many nurses were taking pride in answering the call to save their country. They basked in their new-found glory of being a "healthcare hero," so they would exaggerate things a lot, tending to answer with emotion and not facts. After talking with several of them, I knew they were still in their hotel weeks later and had never been called to go to a hospital and work!

Meanwhile, I worked at a federal hospital that utilizes the Public Health Commissioned Corps of the U.S. Public Health Service, a uniformed service of the U.S. government, like the military, for their daily operations. They work on the frontlines of public health as medical health and engineering professionals to fight disease, conduct research, and care for patients in underserved communities worldwide. Several of them were stationed on the Comfort Ship in New York City. You might remember this as the ship that Governor Andrew Cuomo begged for but never used.

HEALTH AND SCIENCE

Coronavirus patients spend night on Navy hospital ship meant for non-infected New York patients

PUBLISHED SAT, APR 4 2020·3:44 PM EDT | UPDATED SAT, APR 4 2020·4:23 PM EDT

"The Comfort Ship is supposed to treat patients with conditions other than COVID-19 to free up space in overwhelmed New York hospitals. The thousand-bed hospital ship, which arrived in New York City on Monday, has treated 27 patients as of Saturday morning, according to a Navy spokesperson. Hospital leaders in New York City have criticized the Comfort's deployment for not accepting COVID-19 patients and for failing to provide tangible relief to strained hospitals."

- CNBC, April 4th, 2020.

Nurses would come back and tell us that while they had taken care of a few patients, there were nowhere near the numbers the media reported. Regular people were going into hospitals in their neighborhoods and recording empty waiting rooms, but of course, mainstream media never reported this side of the truth. Right from the beginning, red flags kept popping up. I realized that I was witnessing mass propaganda because fear was being pushed 24/7. When you say the same thing repeatedly, people will start to believe you. The biased media kept the death toll ticker scrolling on our phones, TVs, and computer screens. There were never suggestions of what you could do to protect yourself. Immune-boosting tips such as getting fresh air and sunshine,

9

opening the windows in your home to create ventilation and circulation, eating fruits and vegetables, and avoiding processed food and refined sugar to reduce inflammation were never mentioned.

Our talking heads didn't know what to do with this deadly, novel respiratory virus (or did they?), so they asked all of us Americans to "Do your part and stay home to slow the spread." From this point forward, I started to view everything with a critical lens instead of the trustworthy one I had two weeks prior. It was as if something in my soul was crying out for me to pay attention. This seemed like biblical prophecy—how the end times would sound, look, and feel. So I began to really be intentional with my awareness of everything surrounding this virus.

Of course, then the propaganda messaging ramped up. "I wear a mask to protect you. You wear your mask to protect me," became the virtue signal of the day. The people pushing this messaging knew society would eventually realize that COVID was aerosolized and nothing short of a PAPR helmet (a battery powered respirator used to protect against contaminated air) would stop it. So, they'd lie and tell people that the virus is transmitted through droplets that come out of your mouth when you talk or exhale to justify placing a piece of cloth on your face. They said we needed to stay six feet apart with our masks on at all times. Of course, with any small amount of research, you'll find that this is also made-up pseudoscience.

The media and government institutions had everyone paralyzed in fear, with nothing but a thin cloth to hide it. In the beginning, this was easy to go along with. It's only for two weeks, right? It would be chill to lay low for two weeks.

Yeah, sure. My bullsh@t meter was at an all-time high. Being a nurse means so much more to me than just a few letters by my name. It's not only what I do to make a living. The ethics I vowed to uphold are who I am as a person. It is the embodiment of my very being. I care deeply for humanity, and I can't just sit back and not say anything about what was going on behind the scenes, which most Americans couldn't see. It just wasn't in my character. So, I removed my affiliation with the hospital from my Facebook profile and decided to publicly share my research and personal experience on social media.

RARE

Chapter Two

The Misuse of Masks

Suddenly, signs were everywhere saying you must wear a mask if you wanted to enter a business. The circles, placed every six feet to encourage social distancing, quickly followed, and useless plexiglass-lined countertops were at every cash register in the country.

I began researching masks and their efficacy. My healthcare training told me they would only be used on a symptomatic patient, not on the general public, especially if they had no symptoms. At this point, masks weren't easily accessible. Before this, healthcare providers rarely wore them unless we were doing a sterile bedside procedure or an operation (to protect the open wound from contamination). For those instances, the masks came in a sterile kit, giving us another barrier to entry. Other than that, we only wore them with infectious patients like those with TB (or during the flu season as a punishment for opting out of the annual flu shot).

I started my search by looking into basic particle size. When we had a TB (Tuberculosis) patient, we were required to wear an N95 respirator, which filters 0.3-micron particles with a 95% efficiency. TB is an airborne, aerosolized virus, requiring the patient to be in a negative pressure room. Well, how big is the flu virus, then? It's 0.2 microns and the COVID-19 virus has a size of 0.1 microns. Like a lightbulb, it clicked. Our N95 respirators, which are extremely cumbersome and can only be tolerated for short amounts of time, cannot block COVID, which is three times smaller than TB. So, the surgical masks essentially did nothing to protect us, let alone the regular cloth masks people created at home.

I then realized these mandates weren't about keeping people safe. This was about controlling people, providing citizens with a false sense of security, and giving them the illusion of helping their fellow man. I hated everything these masks represented and grew increasingly livid at the idea of masking everybody, especially our kids.

Next, doctors with microphones started talking about wearing masks, repeating that they were safe and effective. I knew they weren't the experts we should be listening to. Sure, they got fit tested for the N95 like I did each year, but they weren't industrial hygienists. So I researched night and day for the experts on mask protocols and efficacy. It was then that I found Kristen Meghan, Stephen Petty, Tammy Clark, TL Peters, and Chris Schaffer. They were highly credentialed industrial hygienists, OSHA experts, and exposure scientists. They also happened to be speaking out against using masks for COVID-19 and showing the peer-reviewed science of why they were ineffective.

Kristen was also a military whistleblower who once worked on the Chicago pandemic preparedness team. She had an impressive resume, as did Tammy Clark, an OSHA whistleblower.

Stephen, a forensics, exposure, and PPE expert, would go on to create the Petty Podcast in July 2021 on YouTube, which he used to further spread his message that masks simply weren't working and what we could do that would make a difference. However, that was short-lived due to censorship, and he moved the topic onto a Rumble channel so he could speak uncensored. It was unbelievable the role big tech played in censoring the truth from the experts.

In May 2020, President Trump talked about his experience taking hydroxychloroquine for fourteen days along with zinc and azithromycin. This is when I first became familiar with an upstate New York physician treating high-risk patients with a multisequence drug approach, Dr. Vladimir "Zev" Zelenko. By March, he had successfully treated over 500 patients and appealed to the President to adopt these protocols. The drugs are well known as are their side effects, and they are cheap.

Dr. Zelenko was adamant in upholding his oath to compassionately treat patients. After all, when in the history of medicine have we told the world they could test positive for a deadly disease, but would have to wait until they show signs of dying (i.e., turning blue or having severe shortness of breath) to come into the hospital only to be treated with an experimental medication, Remdesivir? Our go-to respiratory distress drugs like Solu-Medrol, for example, lower inflammation, and nebulized albuterol, which opens the airways, were not recommended for COVID. It was mind-blowing how, even though the provider was wearing a mask, they stopped nebulizing patients (which was best for them) to lower their own exposure.

Unbeknownst to me at the time, Dr. Zelenko should not have been alive. Two years prior, he was diagnosed with pulmonary artery sarcoma, a type of lung cancer with a 100% mortality rate. Everyone who develops this rare cancer is at a high-risk of dying, and he was only functioning with one lung and still willing to uphold his oath to compassionately treat patients. At the same time, most providers took a back seat because this was "novel," and they were waiting for our alphabet agencies to tell them how to practice medicine. Meanwhile, people were dying. It was a travesty. Public accolades meant nothing to Dr. Zelenko. He would later tell me he wondered why God spared him. We both knew this was why.

It is important to recognize that two different diseases

are at play here. One is COVID-19, which most people handle like a cold and the other is the progression to a life-threatening disease called acute respiratory distress syndrome (ARDS) and how they justified putting people on the ventilator in the early days. His protocol didn't treat ARDS, but it certainly kept people from developing it. He explained that hydroxychloroquine opens the door and lets the zinc go inside the cell to wreak havoc on the virus. He postulated that azithromycin prevents a secondary bacterial infection which could happen when someone is overwhelmed with a virus. So he thought, let's combine the three of them. It made perfect sense to me!

In July, a group of practicing physicians called American Frontline Doctors held their white coat summit at our nation's capital, speaking on the use of hydroxychloroquine and the effects the lockdowns would have on mental health.

I was ecstatic and hopeful for early treatment but became disappointed pretty quickly. Where were my fellow nurses and doctors? The regular foot soldiers on the frontlines of medicine were nowhere to be found when it came to voicing their disagreements with the state of the mandates and the Patients' Bill of Rights being stripped away. Were they not doing the same research that I was? Or was it simply easier to be complacent and "go with the flow"? Anytime I tried engaging in scientific inquiry with my fellow healthcare workers, I quickly realized the political party they aligned with. Those who didn't like President Trump parroted he was promoting disinformation by suggesting there were early treatment options. The others would parrot that this was a "novel respiratory virus" and, "We're doing the best we can." Still, almost three years later (as of this writing), there are no medical institutions or universities that have sponsored an early treatment protocol. This was the beginning of our ethical principles being compromised. The masks simply became a symbol of the fear-mongering and propaganda slowly eating away at the fibers of our society.

The government bodies in charge of these mandates also ignored the problem of putting a reusable cloth over one of the most vulnerable parts of your body. Over time, a mask begins to function as a Petri dish, and the bacterial contaminants that collect on the mask through touching it, being breathed on, etc., can make you sick. How many masks did you see being pulled out of the bottom of a purse? Or hung up on the rearview mirror? Or placed on the dinner table? Any little bit of efficacy they had was gone as these loose practices rendered them completely useless.

My medical community on Facebook was filled with pictures of people wearing masks and big circles framing their faces stating, "healthcare hero." I couldn't bear to look at these virtue signaling images. Yet, at the same time, I also knew these people deserved a certain amount of grace and mercy. For many of these seasoned nurses, this was the first time that society had given them any amount of public appreciation, and they were simply basking in the excitement of it all. This would, of course, be no excuse for their silence as patients' rights, their constitutional rights, and our ethical principles were beginning to be stripped away one by one. My research pointed to the uselessness of masks and the only time I condone the wearing of one for a short amount of time is if someone is coughing or sneezing uncontrollably (to prevent large droplets from landing on someone else). But what about people who can't wear masks for medical or psychological reasons? Should we not allow them to go into society, get medical care, or shop for food? What kind of message is this sending to our kids? How will this affect our babies' cognitive growth when they need to see facial reactions early in their lives? What about the fear and anxiety this created for our vulnerable mental health population? And what about those recovering from alcohol and narcotics?

All this so that people could feel like they had some kind of power over the COVID situation? Or was it being done to condition them to accept anything the government said just because they said it? Blind faith. I knew it was the latter. It was clear to me at this point that most people succumbed to the propaganda messaging and put their faith in men. The government became their god.

At this same time, the CDC was telling us that healthcare workers were considered low-risk if they spent less than fifteen minutes in close contact with a COVID-positive patient, even if they had no PPE. So how does walking past somebody in the supermarket without a mask for two seconds increase my risk so dramatically that I need to wear a mask in 110-degree Arizona heat? It was asinine to me.

Schools were shut down after spring break. I remember thinking, "Why are we shutting down all the schools over this?" We already knew the children weren't at risk. It was our elderly we needed to protect. It seemed obvious to me that the fear the government and mainstream media were putting on these children would begin affecting them. After all, we told healthy children they needed to stay home because they could kill someone and not even know it, and if they left the house, they needed to wear a mask because they could kill grandma by the mere act of breathing. How could this not affect them horribly? So, I started to educate myself on the psychosocial and psychological effects this could cause.

My youngest son was ten when all of this was happening, the same age I was when the AIDS epidemic came onto the scene. There was so much we didn't know back then. All they told us was that it was mostly a gay man's disease. I remember going to my cousin's funeral with my mom. "He was gay and died of AIDS; surely, his gay friends would be there," I thought. At that young age, I wondered, "Can you get it from hugging somebody?" I expressed my concern to my mom, who told me we had nothing to worry about. My mom is a strong woman, and I was comforted by her words. And I hugged everyone at the funeral who wanted a hug!

Years would go by, and still, so many people were confused about how you could contract it. The difference was our media back then wasn't pushing a narrative of fear 24/7.

Now, I constantly think about what my life would have been like if the same coordinated propaganda effort to incite fear had been made with AIDS. What would my childhood have been like if I thought I could kill somebody just by breathing on them? What a disgusting thought. Exactly what kind of monster would say this to a child? What would the world look like today if my generation was told that?

The term asymptomatic transmission was now a household phrase. Before the COVID scamdemic, nobody in the medical community used this term because it never had any clinical significance. We don't routinely test people for a disease when they have no symptoms! So I began researching just what it was. I found some information about asymptomatic transmission with the flu, but it was so incredibly rare that it was negligible, so I figured it didn't matter much. Furthermore, if this were true, we would see a lot more sickness worldwide, as it would spread much quicker if people didn't know they were actually sick. Confusing, I know.

"Wow, they are really trying to scare people. This is unbelievable," I thought to myself.

Chapter Three

Life in Lockdown

In our society's attempt to save lives by shutting down the economy and schools, we began to push people further down an isolated rabbit hole, which had tangible effects on people's mental health. Healthcare providers are trained to use Evidence-Based Practice, which is the best available science. Instead, we were using methods we weren't even sure would work. How did our providers allow the government to interfere in the physician-patient relationship and dictate how to practice medicine?

A friend of mine posted on Instagram:

"I just want everyone to understand that a lot of people and a lot of dancers are suffering from suicidal thoughts due to isolation.

Not having any in-person human interaction is really bad for people who suffer from mental health challenges like depression or anxiety. I've had a few dancers confide in me about their thoughts and how scared they are. Living in isolation is not natural for humans. So if you see some of us influencers making videos, maybe first think about why they're doing it. Some of us don't qualify for government assistance.

We need to make money somehow and make it with other people who are negative for COVID-19. Or they need to do something that will give them a break from their mental illness, and creating is just a great outlet. We are all scared. We are all sensitive. We are all suffering. We are all doing our best. Trust me, don't assume and lead with love."

"Amen. Be kind and lead with love." I responded to her post. "It's the enemy's job to confuse us and to make us scared and anxious. Well, no more. The numbers and studies are coming out, showing us isolation is not the answer. Discernment told us that. Stay sane, my brothers and sisters, don't let those that are fearful bully you into believing what you feel in your soul to be true. It's only going to get harder, and we must not let others decide what is right because everyone believes what they believe. Let them."

I decided it was time to talk to my youngest son, Benjamin, about what was going on, so I brought him into the living room so we could talk. I rented the movie Outbreak with Dustin Hoffman.

Then, I told him, "I do not want you to be afraid because if things were really this bad, this is what we would be seeing, people dropping dead in the streets."

"I've never been afraid in my entire life!"

To be honest, this was mostly true. From a young age, whenever he would be scared at night, or his mind was racing, and he couldn't sleep, I would play sermons for him. Messianic pastors, Jonathan Cahn and Discovering the Jewish Jesus, were his favorites. I would remind him that the enemy is trying to get into his spirit, and how we use the Word of God and our faith to combat it.

Throughout his entire life, he never expressed anything even close to resembling fear. He referenced the movie *Jojo Rabbit,* which I had taken him to go see just a few months prior. It is about a ten-year-old boy, my son's age, who, during World War II, discovers his mother is hiding a Jewish girl in her attic. With his imaginary best friend Adolf Hitler, Jojo must confront his blind nationalism as the war rages on. He told me it reminded him of what he saw on TV and how all he would see and hear was fear. We continued our lives normally, except he wasn't currently in school. But, of course, he didn't mind that.

As time progressed, things only got worse. It seemed as if the scientific community had never heard of a respiratory infection and had no idea how they were spread (through your nose and mouth). Tequila-smelling hand sanitizers were everywhere. The MSM (mainstream media) were using the 1918 Spanish Flu pandemic as a talking point to justify masks and lockdowns, but there were distinct differences. First, medications like hydroxychloroquine which exhibits antiviral properties and slows down viral replication, or steroids, like dexamethasone, which lowers inflammation to prevent disease progression, had not yet been invented in 1918. Second, it was the younger population that had a high mortality rate, not the elderly. Third, they found out that masks did not work and why almost a hundred years later, we never used them for any respiratory outbreak.

Working as a critical care nurse in a hospital setting, you prepare to expect the unexpected. Not only are we caring for patients but also for each other. As nurses, we are trained to put our political beliefs aside and care directly for the patient in front of us. During these times, many of the staff were concerned with taking the virus home to their loved ones. Some were forced by their immediate and extended family to get a hotel room for a few weeks until more was learned. That left them coming to work depressed because they hadn't seen their husband or children. A couple of them had babies. This was heartbreaking. Never once did it cross my mind to isolate myself.

This photo accompanied the following Facebook post.

Jodi O'Malley
March 27, 2020 · 🌐   •••

Everyday before I leave for work Benjamin fills up
my water jugs, kisses me and tells me to have "a
good day".

As I was walking out the door I said, "Hold up.
We need to take a picture." He laughed and said,
"why?!" I said to shout you out because of the
kindness and strength you show in these strange
times. So many people are stressed with anxiety
and fear when their loved ones leave to work in
the hospital because of this virus."

He says, "yeah I've been hearing that. I have no
fear over this virus" I said, "Good. Me neither."

But God got me💜

When I looked at the picture later I was bummed
because Benjamin was in the shadow. I wished I
got a better one then the Aaronic blessing came
to mind...

Numbers 6:24-26
24 "The Lord bless you and keep you;
25 The Lord make His face shine upon you,
And be gracious to you;
26 The Lord [a]lift up His countenance upon you,
And give you peace." '

I try everyday in everyway to stay in God's plan for my life and allow Him to use me in anyway He sees fit. The amount of peace and discernment that comes with that is a power unlike no other. People always ask me, "how do I know I'm following His path?" It's easy (except when the enemy disguises itself as a tall, dark, handsome man😳😍) But like any relationship you foster and put in the effort to get to know someone the easier it became. I recognize Him wherever I go! He lays something on my heart I follow it. When it's met with anxiety, uncertainty and questions I shut it out and I remember God's word..

◄ 2 Timothy 1:7 ►
King James Version
For God hath not given us the spirit of fear; but of power, and of love, and of a sound mind.

I used to think that it wasn't important to read the bible. In the last few years I've learned how wrong I was. He is The Word.

John 1 King James Version (KJV)
1 In the beginning was the Word, and the Word was with God, and the Word was God.
14 And the Word was made flesh, and dwelt among us, (and we beheld his glory, the glory as of the only begotten of the Father,) full of grace and truth.

In the last couple weeks it's felt like I'm living in the twilight zone lol. I've always known that most people are sheep. The ability the enemy has to control their thoughts and minds and confuse even the "believers" is phenomenal. I see clearly the ones who are controlled by the evil spirit and I recognize those living in the Spirit.

Isaiah 52:6 (CJB) Therefore my people will know my name; therefore on that day they will know that I, the one speaking - here I am!"

In the past I've stayed away from saying that I'm saved or born again because of negative thoughts associated with it. But not anymore. These are days my preacher spoke about 40 years ago. There must be a great revival for us to regain the power back from the enemy. It has controlled earth long enough and in the days to come the world will see it. But God always uses evil for good.

As a society we've allowed evil to be mistaken for good and good for evil.This is "The Great Awakening". Be not fearful of COVID-19 my friends. Be afraid of what you're allowing it to do to your soul.

1 Samuel 25:6 "And thus you shall greet him: 'Peace be to you, and peace be to your house, and peace be to all that you have."

#yeshua #yahweh #YHWH #messiah #jesus #thegreatawakening #revival #peace See less

 73   27 Comments 2 Shares

At the same time, our hospital, and many others around the nation, began to shut down non-essential surgeries in preparation for the influx of patients we were led to believe was coming. On March 15, 2020, the American Hospital Association, Association of American Medical Colleges, Children's Hospital Association, and Federation of American Hospitals collectively wrote a letter to the US Surgeon General asking them to reconsider this blanket shutdown approach. Often, if these procedures are delayed or canceled, the person's condition worsens rapidly and can even be life-threatening. This was fundamentally wrong.

What was alarming to me was the number of people not coming to the hospital for treatment. The patient's that my hospital serves are Native Americans. The primary issues we tended to see at our facility were diabetic emergencies, bowel issues, diabetic wounds, heart problems, rare cancers, and abscesses, not to mention alcoholism and mental health emergencies. I knew that shutting down the non-essential surgeries for even two weeks would result in many undiagnosed illnesses and diseases and greatly impact how many lives would be lost to these otherwise preventable diseases.

Three months had passed in Arizona, and I still didn't see COVID patients flooding the hallways of local hospitals. Yet the mainstream media kept talking about it. Still, during the spring of 2020, our hospital was a ghost town.

This really troubled me. These problems didn't evaporate because of COVID. If anything, the lockdown situation exacerbated these problems. And since everyone was afraid to come to the hospital, these problems could become life-threatening if they were not treated early. That is why these procedures and surgeries are performed before they become emergencies.

Before COVID, many colonoscopies were performed, in which polyps and tumors would be noticed. But now, even cancer patients were not receiving surgeries or diagnostic procedures at the hospital. For example, our hospital partners with Mayo Clinic to provide oncology services to the Native American community, which often develops rare forms of cancer. Therefore, Mayo Clinic was especially interested in caring for and studying this population. Why they weren't interested in being a center of excellence in early treatment for COVID is beyond me.

Treatments for appendix, gallbladder removals, and abscesses, all of which can make a person extremely sick and septic to the point of being life-threatening if not taken care of right away, ceased.

I may not have been afraid of COVID, but the rest of the world seemed to be. And this, to me, was the scariest part of it all, or so I thought at the time. I can't find words to describe the concern I felt for these patients and the community. It is common for them to live in multigenerational households, and I always had it in the back of my mind how quarantining the healthy with the sick when they put the reservations on lockdown would affect the ones we were supposed to be protecting. It made zero sense to do that, and it is against Public Health Policy 101. But I pushed on and reminded myself daily to have faith and trust in the Lord.

make sure you test positive for faith
keep distance from doubt
isolate yourself from fear
and trust God through it all.

All the while, we were being delivered food from the community because we were "healthcare heroes," even if the hospital (by lack of diagnostic procedures, early treatment, and surgeries) was now beginning to risk the lives of those we were supposed to protect. My heart was breaking. I just knew in my spirit it would get much worse, and I began to prepare myself mentally and spiritually.

This whole "healthcare hero" thing was hard for me to accept. We literally didn't work. We just sat there watching movies all night because everybody was so paralyzed by fear that they weren't coming into the hospital. One of the many benefits of being a federal employee during this time is we received a 25% bonus for hazard duty pay, and we were guaranteed our forty hours. They couldn't send us home because of "low workload" and force us to use our paid time off if we didn't want our paychecks affected. Dozens of nurses who worked for private hospitals would share with me that they were "low workloaded," meaning they would get a call a couple hours before their scheduled shift saying to stay home, which forced them to use their paid time off. Plus, their hospitals were asking if they wanted to take early retirement or unpaid maternity leave (if pregnant). They were also approving nurses to take twelve-week travel assignments to the "hot spots." This would later come to bite them as many experienced nurses accepted their offer.

And in regards to public health policies, I knew that having healthy people stay home and paralyze them with fear, which lowers their immune system by creating a stress response, not to mention quarantining the healthy with the sick, was not going to be good for a variety of reasons.

It's not good for the family unit if the head of the household can't go out and collect a paycheck. People who struggled with alcohol addiction couldn't attend their AA meetings (which many do nightly), and our elderly population, which thrives off of routine and personal interaction with family and friends, was just grounded. I saw domestic violence and sexual abuse soar, and the whole time we're getting this free food sent to us because we're "heroes."

I distinctly remember one mother who brought in her eleven-month-old baby. She told me that every time she changed his diaper, he screamed and pushed her hands away. She just knew something was wrong, so she rushed him to the ER. She told me of her struggle to find childcare so she could work. Her daycare was forced to shut down. Her son's friend had been living with them for a couple of years because of a bad home situation, and he offered to babysit. It took two nurses to hold the baby down while the mother was consoling him so the physician could examine him. He was clearly sexually assaulted. I have no words to describe what that moment was like when the doctor had to tell her that. She screamed and cried out. It was awful. I told my colleagues to brace for more heartbreaking tragedies. They knew it too.

The media at that time was full of healthcare hero stories but, in my opinion, it was only to distract the medical community from what was actually taking place. Overnight, hospital administrators around the country were stripping away the Patient's Bill of Rights, which is intended to protect you from restraint and seclusion, allowing for an advocate to be there with you, your right to be prayed over, etc., and our ethical principles were compromised.

The CDC said a person was out of quarantine fourteen days after first testing positive, and we were keeping COVID-positive patients away from their advocate/family/friends for weeks. The right to religious freedom and having a chaplain pray with you went out the window. Our religious leaders closed their doors to the public in their time of need! The right to informed consent and compassionate care (like early treatment) never happened because the only medication that was given out, like candy, was Remdesivir, and early treatment was censored. If patients refused it, they had no other options, thanks to our very own Dr. Anthony Fauci and the National Institutes of Health (NIH) and their partners in crime, the CDC and FDA. The right to try off-label medications (of their choosing and with their physician's approval) didn't happen. This was because their Chief of Staff or pharmacists told our physicians that off-label use medications were not to be used for COVID. Why? Was it because they didn't fall in line with the financial incentive of using the CMS (Centers for Medicaid Services) Remdesivir treatment plan? For the first time in healthcare history, physicians were prevented from practicing medicine, and hospitals were given a bonus payout to use an experimental medication on all COVID positive patients that met the criteria. It was mind-blowing that just a little bit of research, instead of being glued to the television fear porn, could've changed this narrative. Our profession was being celebrated globally for the first time. And at the same time, they were taking away the autonomy of providers to practice medicine. Plus, they were coming up with all kinds of crazy, anti-scientific measures like stay home and quarantine. Don't go outside. Don't get sunshine. Police caution tape was placed around playground equipment. I still can't believe it happened.

RARE

34

Chapter Four

Lord, I Can't Do This Anymore!

Our hospital operated more like a military hospital where most of the management staff were in temporary acting positions. They were constantly moving through the ranks and regularly getting new assignments. This is how the USPHS (United States Public Health Service) Commissioned Corps works, which, in my opinion, does not translate to safe, quality care. I say that because most of their subordinates are civilian federal employees, and once you're in the system, it takes an act of congress to get fired. They don't have the authority in this world, like in the military, where nurses and doctors must follow orders or risk being insubordinate.

One of the projects my supervisor was working on was instituting a telehealth program for our healthcare center. When I walked into work one night, she was waiting for me. She handed me a manual and asked, "Jodi, I was wondering if you would be willing to run the nurse hotline tonight. This is my baby. I've been working on it for so long, and right now, it seems like the right time for us to try and roll it out. And I really want someone with the clinical experience and the assessment skills you have to help guide people over the phone."

"Absolutely," I told her. "I'd be honored."

This honestly felt pretty good because I was new to the Float Pool Department, which meant that the hospital trusted my clinical judgment and assessment skills on whether or not a patient should come to the ER to be seen.

A requirement of working in the ER was that you needed strong clinical assessment skills. I handled all of those calls for the night. Even then, they didn't want symptomatic people to come in. There was no course of treatment other than managing your symptoms. Like, if you have a sore throat, take sore throat medication. If you have a cough, take cough medication, that kind of thing. It was pretty basic, really. I did that for a couple more shifts before they got a call center to take over, and to my knowledge, no one died at home.

Next, the check-in tent was put into operation, and on the first night, I was also asked if I could run that. So we set up outside as patients would enter, and I would determine if they would be placed in the "clean" or "dirty" ER. The "clean" side was for everybody who didn't have any symptoms of a respiratory illness. They would then be placed into our pre-op holding area as that room was now available since we weren't doing any surgeries.

The "dirty" side was for everybody who did have respiratory symptoms. This was the hospital's attempt to mitigate exposure and prevent COVID from spreading to all patients.

"Was it the flu or COVID-19? Many of us will never know because most people stayed home and recovered. But for those that are worried, they are passionate and appalled that people aren't taking quarantine and social distancing seriously enough. The majority of our patients are receptive to education and are easily assured. My major concern for those that have mental health issues, what this will do to them. I fear psychosis and psychotic breaks will soar. I fear for the safety of those that are in abusive relationships, and what's going to happen to them when there's no money left." And I wrote here, "our census is low and so are the acuity levels. Less than a dozen people have qualified for testing and we are still awaiting results. Takes three to five days.

No one has tested positive. Our population are generally obese with diabetes and kidney issues. If you don't want to respond here, send me a PM. I want to hear your experiences firsthand. Thank you for taking the time to respond and share your thoughts. I seriously can't believe how much has changed in the last few weeks. Just doesn't seem real. Many blessings,
Jodi."

- Jodi O'Malley, Facebook, 2020.

"What in the world is happening?" I thought to myself. Over 365 times in the Bible, one scripture for each day, there's a verse that calls Christians to hold faith over fear. We should not fear this world because it's not our home. It's ultimately a small blip on the journey through eternity. We are to love, be kind, show grace and mercy, and to be vigilant. As healthcare providers, we are to uphold our ethical principles and oath to *do no harm* and to practice medicine using the best available science. Exactly what physicians like Dr. Zelenko and American Frontline Doctors were doing.

I spent a lot of time in the next few weeks just listening to experts and reading their studies. I would also spend significant time in prayer, asking God for signs of how and where He wanted me to proceed. After getting the clarification I was looking for, I immediately started to sound the alarm to my Facebook community, telling my friends and family that the handling of this was nothing more than a hoax. I posted articles and studies, trying to give the best scientific data I could. And every time I found something worthy to share, nobody wanted to debate me. All I ever heard back was that the masks were better than nothing and, therefore, we should all do our part and wear them. So, this is how we do science now? Whatever happened to evidence-based practice? I tried to have meaningful, educated conversations with people who only wanted to argue, but I hit a breaking point. "Lord, I can't do this anymore."

"After spending over 10,000 hours educating people on this virus, I'm drained. What's not pictured is my recent crying outburst to anyone who asks how I'm doing. A man I like is too afraid to see me because the positive cases in Arizona have spiked, and I'm a nurse. Some friends that I love and respect can't seem to pick up the phone and have an intelligent conversation, but want to try and pick me apart on social media. Everyone wants to argue. Every time, I want to walk away from social media and keep my advice and opinion limited to those in my circle, so as to not be the receiver of ridicule, hateful speech, that's sometimes bordering on evil. I am sent witness to continue. He gives me a testimony, and it comes from the oddest places sometimes, but I know it's God talking to me. Being energized with the Holy Ghost is a very unique and undeniable feeling that everyone needs in their life. If you haven't felt that before, please ask God to give it to you. We're going to need to be armed with it in these last days ahead. If you've ever wondered what people meant by the end of the world, the rapture, the mark of the beast, tribulation or Armageddon, the book of Revelation or the book of Daniel, watch the video below. Be informed. There is no need to suffer like so many will."

- Jodi O'Malley, June 24, 2020

I continued in another post detailing the CDC's position on a nurse being in close proximity to a COVID positive patient with limited PPE.

> *"I am an ER nurse who cares deeply for the holistic wellbeing of people, and I'm imploring you to wake up, America. I have been fighting what I thought to be a virus for the last six months, literally living and breathing it every day. But that's not what I've been fighting at all. I'm fighting your willingness to comply based on what the CDC and your political party tells you. I've been compromising my air and now they want you to compromise yours. The media pushes anything out and you're so willing to believe it. The CDC is who everyone wants to quote, okay, well quote this. CDC QUOTE ABOUT SPENDING 15 MINUTES AROUND A PATIENT WITH LIMITED PPE"*
>
> *- Jodi O'Malley, Facebook, 2020*

A friend of mine would respond to this post, stating, "My Arizona hospital's full of COVID patients, but ironically, a lot of them aren't even there for that reason. We are doing blitz testing of all patients, so of course we are getting more positive diagnosis', like having a 20 year old patient come in due to head trauma after he crashes his motorcycle and find out two days later when we get his swab back that he's also positive for COVID. No symptoms though. We get so many of those cases."

It may sound strange, but even with all the craziness that was going on in early 2020, I never had any fear of this virus. For one thing, I was certain I had it already, and I was healed and received antibodies from it. Plus, my faith won't allow the spirit of fear to stay in me very long. But my faith would indeed be tested many times before this was all over.

The months progressed with more fear and virtue signaling. If only we had a vaccine, or so was the thought of half the country at the time. Me? I was not so convinced. I'd been keeping up with a number of doctors and nurses who had ample evidence that the vaccines would cause problems over time, and for some, those problems were imminent.

And as each day passed, the corruption and misdeeds I was witnessing became unbearable. Enough was enough. I heard the term "follow the money," and that is what led me to know that mainstream media, FDA, CDC, NIH, Facebook, Twitter, Instagram, universities, Big Pharma, and the lobbyists were all controlled by opposition to any competing narrative that didn't include the vaccine as the savior.

It was around this time I learned that Emergency Use Authorization can only be given when certain statutory criteria have been met, including that there are no adequate, approved, and available alternatives and that alone was precisely why the misinformation and disinformation campaigns for cheap, safe, effective, off-label use medications, rolled out by these organizations were in full effect.

This, in my opinion, was why the FDA, in June 2020, removed the emergency use authorization for the distribution of hydroxychloroquine from the Strategic National Stockpile based on "new information."

This *new information* was largely based on a study published by the highly regarded medical journal, The Lancet, which was embarrassingly retracted by its authors because of faulty data, but that didn't garner any media attention. It fit against their narrative. So most physicians and pharmacists, as much as you would like to think they keep up on new research, were not aware of this, and I would remind them that the *new information* article was retracted.

In October 2020, I had heard and read enough to know that combination drugs including, hydroxychloroquine and Ivermectin, were something I wanted to have in my medicine cabinet. Combined, these drugs have over a hundred years of data, so their safety profile is well known. This was a "no harm, no foul" type of risk-benefit analysis that everyone should have had a choice in deciding for themselves. It's called autonomy in nursing ethics. According to nurse.org, this is defined as "Recognizing each individual patient's right to self-determination and decision-making. As patient advocates, it is imperative that nurses ensure that patients receive all medical information, education, and options in order to choose the option that is best for them. This includes all potential risks, benefits, and complications to make well-informed decisions.

Once the patient has all the relevant information, the medical and nursing team can make a plan of care in compliance with the medical wishes of the patient.

It is important that nurses support the patient in their medical wishes and ensure that the medical team remembers those wishes. Sometimes, nurses will need to continue to advocate for a patient despite the wishes being verbalized because the medical team might not agree with those wishes."

One of the ER doctors I worked with gave me the website to a doctor who was prescribing these, and they gave it to me prophylactically. Over the course of the next few months, whenever my family and friends would reach out to me sick, I gave them the doctor's number. By this time, not only had I referred patients, but the word-of-mouth of healings— sometimes in just a few hours— would spread (and rightfully so). When something works, people naturally tell their friends and family. They may be censored on social media but not by word-of-mouth marketing.

By this time, I had cared for three waves of COVID in my hospital. June/July 2020, when they locked down the reservation,

December/January 2021 (which was when we rolled out the mass vaccination program to the natives and employees), and then July/August 2021. No one was asked about vaccination status when they arrived in the ER in their triage assessment. I urged leadership to collect this data by including it in the COVID questions asked in triage which would prompt nurses to ask and check the box that they had done so. But to no avail. I would remind my colleagues that we are still in Stage III clinical trials to see how effective and safe it is. It usually takes years in this stage before something is injected into the masses because you can't rush time. So now we should be diligent in recognizing safety signals and reporting them. I hypothesized that the government didn't want to know, they just wanted a "needle in every arm" for their nefarious reasons, and the nurses and doctors didn't want to ask what was behind the push to vaccinate because they injected themselves and couldn't take it back. They volunteered to sign up for the experiment, and it was easier to keep their head in the sand.

A year and a half had passed since COVID was first announced. The "vaccine" was known to be failing (or, as the CDC likes to say, "Breakthrough infections" were occurring). Doctors and nurses didn't seem to be noting safety signals (like chest pain complaints within days of vaccination) and, therefore, not reporting them to VAERS (Vaccine Adverse Event Reporting System). No university or three-letter government agency sponsored an early treatment protocol. Absolutely no hospitals stood up to become a "Center of Excellence for Early Treatment of COVID."

Something had to be done to prevent more innocent people from being hurt. By this time, I personally knew dozens of people who had been successfully treated. My oldest son, JJ, worked as an EMT at the busiest ER in the Valley. He and I would exchange similar stories regularly about what we were seeing happening. It felt like a nightmare. Most of the people came in with anxiety and panic attacks because the fear had been built up, and they were mentally breaking down. It is important to have perspective. For example, the majority of ER nurses' patients are sent home, while an ICU nurse's patient is the sickest of the sick. There were multitudes of people who professed to know a nurse or doctor and then proceeded to tell me what they were told (which they took as gold), only to find out that one works in urgent care and the other is a foot doctor.

I couldn't take it anymore. Who would help me make this right? My supervisor told me that I couldn't talk about any medications to patients that they weren't prescribed and that there were talks of some bitter ICU nurses reporting me to the Nursing Board for even talking about Ivermectin. I laughed when she told me that and told her I had half a mind to go to the reservation with signs that talked about early treatment. She chuckled and told me, "Please don't do that." It was one of the last conversations we had face-to-face.

Without many outlets to turn to, I approached Project Veritas. I'd seen them months earlier exposing Fox News, Hasbro, CBS, Facebook, etc., and I started following them on Instagram. I liked their hard-hitting, no-nonsense, *we never settle* style, and I thought I'd be comfortable working with them. I'll admit, I had no idea how they did their work. I just figured if they wanted my story, they'd send me a few questions, have me talk into my camera a little, and I'd just send that over.

So I reached out via email. My subject line read: RN for Federal Government HHS/IHS. Within hours, I received an email from one of their journalists, named Chloe. We talked on the phone for at least an hour when she asked, "What exactly is the story you're trying to tell here?"

I let loose all at once. "It's everything. The masks don't work. Social distancing is based on bunk science. The PCR tests are inaccurate. There are sexual assaults on one-year-olds because the mom had to leave them with "the family friend" since daycares are closed, and she needs to work! Suicides are on the rise from the isolation people are going through. There is an increase in drug overdoses. I'm seeing neurological and heart issues that signal safety concerns due to these vaccines, and they are going unnoticed and under-reported! There's so much I need to tell, Chloe."

By this point, I had seen so much firsthand and heard so much more from others that I struggled to get my story together. I couldn't seem to put into words all the things I had seen. I was crying and overwhelmed.

"Well, Jodi, do you have any hard evidence of this stuff?" she replied.

"No, I don't."

She was very sweet. "You know," she began, "this is your story to tell, not ours. We can't put it together for you."

All of this was happening, and yet, I couldn't prove any of it. While there were plenty of testimonies from nurses and doctors all over the world, nobody would believe any of us without proof. I knew I couldn't break HIPPA. I could lose my nursing license and my livelihood. Feelings of panic overcame me after I got off the call. Can I trust them? Can they tell others what I just told them? What did I just do?! I told her everything, and I'm a federal employee! I was panic-stricken and didn't tell anyone that I had reached out to them. I decided I'd just keep it to myself a little longer.

Chapter Five

COVID Hits Home

It was just another ordinary Saturday night in the summer of 2021. As I drove to work, I listened to a sermon, as I usually would. The twenty-minute drive with Messianic Rabbi Jonathan Cahn, a Jewish believer in Jesus the Messiah (or Yeshua, as we refer to Him), helped me gather my thoughts and get my mind in order.

I found out about Jonathan Cahn from my sister back in 2014 when I started to feel indifferent about celebrating Christmas and Easter holidays. This was unusual for me, and I discussed that with her. She confided that she was feeling the same way. We began researching these traditions since the Bible could not provide any direct guidance. What we learned about the history of these celebrations deeply affected us. Both of these holidays are rooted in pagan beliefs; the Christmas tree adorned with ornaments and the Easter Bunny and eggs had nothing to do with Christ our Savior. Satan loves to take things that people construe as good and use them for evil. Yeshua is rarely ever mentioned in the homes of people during Christmas. And Easter morning, after church service (if one attends), is celebrated with an egg hunt. As a little girl, I remember hearing my pastor, Sister Kelly, preach about the end times and that when the Jews start to recognize that Yeshua is the Messiah, how powerful it would be.

She wasn't mistaken because when I first heard Rabbi Jonathan Cahn preach, I was immediately impacted. The Old Testament is called the Tanakh, and the first five books are The Torah, which was originally written in Hebrew. To hear a Jew, translating the Torah from Hebrew to English is powerful as their language is so different, and it demonstrates how the Word (Jesus) was always there since the beginning. I then learned that what I thought was the Last Supper with Yeshua and the disciples was really Jesus celebrating Passover. I was in awe! Yeshua was celebrating the Feasts that the Lord commanded, and He said in Matthew 5:17, "Do not think that I came to destroy the Law or the Prophets. I did not come to destroy but to fulfill."

In Leviticus 23, Adonai tells us what we are commanded to celebrate "for all time." Since the moment I learned this, these are the holidays we celebrate, and every single one revolves around Yeshua.

When I arrived at the hospital, before getting out of the car, I prayed, "Lord, please guide my heart, mind, and tongue as I serve the staff and patients I oversee tonight," as was customary for me to do, and tonight was no different.

Between the Rabbi's teaching and my prayers, I smiled as recent memories of happy times with family played over in my mind. I had just had the week off with my dad, who flew in from Chicago, and my daughter and grandson were also visiting from Hawaii. It was wonderful to have my family together and be "normal" in a world gone crazy. The brief respite from my job felt so nice. I wanted to linger in it a little longer, yet I knew I had to begin mentally preparing for my return to work, which was mere moments away.

As I got closer and closer to the hospital, my thoughts moved on to the unknown. Having been away for seven days, I wondered exactly what I would be stepping into. We saw a surge of people coming into our hospital over the previous two months, and a week is a lot of time for things to change. The uncertainty of how stressful my shift would be and the blistering summer heat of Arizona made me not want to be anywhere near that hospital. As I got out of my car, I couldn't help but notice the gorgeous sunset with bright orange hues gently looming over the horizon, pulling one last tug on my heart to be normal for just a few seconds longer.

Gone were the days when you could come and go from the hospital easily. Now, there was a tent where we had to check in first. But it was 114 degrees out, so they moved the check-in table just inside the ER.

"Hello," I smiled.

"Good evening," the nurse at the door replied. "You know the drill. Have you had any fever?"

"No."

"Any chills? Nausea? Back pain?"

"No, I don't have any symptoms."

She continued asking all the questions, you know, all the classic tell-tale signs of COVID like diarrhea, nausea, and back pain, until I had answered 'no' to each of them. Then she handed me the obligatory mask we were required to wear, holding the part that covers the nose and mouth with her unclean hands. I always replied, "Thanks. But I'll grab my own." I would don it and then immediately place it under my chin.

Inside, I asked the triage nurse who felt the same about the handling of this virus, "Did they add vaccine status to the list of COVID questions?"

"No," she laughed, "Do you think they want to know they are failing?"

I just shook my head in disgust and proceeded to the elevator.

I would always enter the hospital without a mask on. That was just my practice. Of course, I had my nightly paper cup filled with coffee in my hand as an excuse for why I wasn't wearing my mask over my mouth and nose. I felt that if people could see my face and smile, they would get a subliminal message that I wasn't concerned, and that would help them not be so afraid of this whole thing.

The emergency room was busier than usual that night. The triage nurse sat outside the entry door, behind this three-foot wall partition, so they could see out in front of everything. The waiting room, no larger than fifteen by twenty feet, had some plastic chairs that we could move around easily. That night was so busy that people were stacked on top of each other.

I passed through the ER, turned, and walked through the old, dingy hallway towards the elevators, as I'd done hundreds of times before. It was kind of depressing, honestly. The 1970's Pepto Bismol pink bathrooms and psych ward green tile on the walls showed just how long it had been since getting an updated look. The building was almost a hundred-years-old, definitely not a cheerful-looking place, and hadn't been painted in forever, as evidenced by flecks of peeling paint on the wall.

Next, I passed the pharmacy window and noticed a lot of people waiting in the hallway to pick up their prescriptions. As was typical by this time, they were each standing on the small circles placed every six feet to "help" with social distancing. Ugh, I had to hold back the vomit that crept into my throat, knowing full well this does nothing.

As I stepped onto the elevator, everything seemed average for another night in a federal hospital during the COVID era. However, when I got upstairs, my world rapidly changed, beginning a new season that was anything but the "normal" I'd been forced to accept to that point.

I entered the small office to get a report from the day shift supervisor. "Hey, how's it going?" I asked with a smile.

"Just another day in paradise," she replied sarcastically. "So listen, Angel has been admitted to the ICU with COVID."

I gasped in a short breath of air. "What? Oh my gosh!"

My mind flashed back in time. Only two weeks prior, our

pharmacist came onto our unit auctioning off the last few COVID vaccine doses she had left before they expired at the end of our shift. Angel was my coworker in the ICU and had just returned from leave, having spent some time off due to surgery. From prior conversations, I knew she was reluctant to get the vaccine because of her traditional Native beliefs.

"Okay, guys, I got three shots left before I've gotta throw it away when day shift comes in. Who wants it?" the pharmacist asked.

We all looked around the room at each other, and I spun around in my chair with my head down, looking at the keyboard. No one was jumping at the opportunity.

A couple of nurses chimed in, "Come on, you guys haven't gotten your shots yet! Just go get it done."

"Nobody should be coerced to participate in an experiment," I mumbled quietly, keeping my head down on the computer monitor I was working from. I thought to myself, "That's not what we do. I might add that coercion to participate in an experiment, a poorly run one, is against our ethical principles. It's everybody's right to choose." But I knew my opinion was in the minority that night, and they'd heard my views countless times before.

Jodi O'Malley
July 22, 2021 · 🌐 ···

No one was sure what our risks were in 2020 and we still went to work. We chose to go back, day in and day out without knowing what was walking through the door. We took care of everyone without exception.

If you're a health professional and encouraging of people being forced to take a brand new technology and drug that has never before been injected into humans until last year and applaud the coercion taking place by taking away their livelihoods if they don't participate in this phase 3 experimental study you should be ashamed. We don't force anyone to take anything!

Everyone should have a choice! This is America! And this is a crime against humanity!

There was already a nursing shortage prior to 2020. Just imagine what our hospitals will become if up to 50% decide to leave.
Be careful what you stand for.

And just like that, three CNAs followed her off our unit and got their first dose. Now, exactly two weeks later, here we sat, the same day that Angel was supposed to get her second injection, and she'd been admitted as a patient into the hospital.

As I received report, I found out she didn't require oxygen or anything critical, but they had her in the ICU to be safe.

"They admitted her at ten o'clock last night," the going off-duty supervisor continued. "She tested positive for COVID, but she does not have any real symptoms. No fever. No cough."

"If she doesn't need oxygen, why is she even here?" I asked, confused.

"Well, she's not feeling well. They started her on Remdesivir."

"Remdesivir? She doesn't even need oxygen. She doesn't meet the basic requirements for it!"

"I know, but that's the plan, apparently."

I stood there for a moment, dazed by all I'd just heard. She had just received the first dose of the "vaccine" two weeks prior, and now she was positive for COVID. "What brought her here if she wasn't having problems breathing?" I thought to myself.

Angel was small in stature, morbidly obese, and square in shape. She didn't smile a whole lot, but on the rare occasion when she did, it was the sweetest smile surrounded by big, chunky cheeks—so big that they made her kind eyes appear very tiny. I never once saw her without her beautiful jet-black hair pulled back in a ponytail.

She was a stoic, strong, quiet, intelligent person and a very sweet soul. Having been a CNA for almost twenty years at this hospital, she was also coveted by all the nurses on our floor as she was clearly the best one we had there. She worked hard and was always going into COVID-positive patients' rooms to answer their call lights without hesitation. She'd spend a lot of time with them, making sure they were comfortable, taking care of each patient as if they were her own family members. As a fellow Native American, these were her people, and she cared for them immensely.

Because of the National Emergency Act signed on March 13, 2020, there was a significant decrease in the level of care and charting parameters we were required to provide during 2020 and 2021 (and continues as of this writing, allowing hospitals to be liability-free because of the "pandemic"). Throughout the COVID years, many nurses distanced themselves from patients, only doing the bare minimum. Even the doctors weren't going into rooms to assess the patients, opting to chart, ". . . to lessen COVID exposure, report received from nurse." And prescribing remotely.

Nurses were doing less charting because we were under pandemic protocols and didn't have to chart hourly (pain, potty, position, etc.), which reminds you to check on your patient's needs like we normally would have. Also, lots of doctors changed vital sign checks to every twelve hours instead of every four. This all led to patients, on average, receiving less care from the nursing staff than they would have pre-COVID, but Angel just wasn't like that. When everyone else was significantly limiting their time in patient rooms, Angel always maintained the same level of care. She was still loving on her patients, keeping them as safe and comfortable as possible.

I loved working with her as my nurse's aide. She settled your nerves when you had a patient crashing because you knew that she would be able to help set everything up and get you what you needed. She never complained. She didn't talk badly about people. If somebody did something wrong or said something bad, she would just shake her head and walk away, refusing to participate in the gossip.

So when I saw her now as a patient, I wanted to care for her like she would have cared for her patients. I knew that this all needed to be documented. At the very least, a safety signal should be sent to VAERS (Vaccine Adverse Event Reporting System) to indicate possible side effects from the COVID vaccine she'd taken.

I asked Angel's nurse, "Is this being reported to VAERS? This happened within two weeks of vaccination."

"I don't think we need to do that. I don't think it's reportable. They're telling me it's COVID."

"Yeah, but how many patients have come into the hospital two weeks after their vaccine, testing positive for COVID?" I questioned as the concern in my voice grew. "There's something wrong here. How did she survive all this time, eighteen months caring for patients, in close contact with COVID, being social, and going out to bars, but now all of a sudden, after a shot, she's sick and in the hospital?" I asked.

She shrugged. No one ever wanted to go down that line of critical thinking and questioning. Like I said before, most of them got injected, so to recognize an adverse reaction only meant that they could be affected themselves.

Next, I went to Angel's room to see her, so I could get an idea of how she was doing. As I entered the glass doors to that corner room, I saw her sitting on the edge of her bed. It was probably a more comfortable position for her than lying down. I immediately noticed that she was breathing okay but didn't look so good. We made jokes back and forth with each other, just like we'd always done. Her vitals were fine, and she didn't need oxygen. I really didn't understand why they admitted her at this point.

"So, what brought you in?" I asked.

"I just.. I'm not feeling good," she told me. "Ya know, they want to give me Remdesivir." Then she asked, "I want to try those meds you were talking about before. What were they called?"

"It's on the FLCCC (Front Line COVID-19 Critical Care Alliance) protocol."

She pulled out her phone and went to the hospital protocol on that site. "I'm already on all but a few of these things. If you were in my situation, would you take them?"

"Absolutely, Angel," I told her. "Honestly, if I were talking to a member of my family right now, I would tell them to get up and leave because you don't require oxygen. But, then, I'd say to find somebody who will prescribe this protocol for you. The truth is, we're not going to treat you here. We're just going to give you Remdesivir, and you and I both know how that stuff works."

Remdesivir was an emergency use authorization, a.k.a. investigational medication for COVID. It was known to tank heart rates at least twenty beats from the baseline, interfere with kidney and liver function, and included an average length of hospital stay of five days to three weeks.

"Yeah, you're right. I'm going to leave here in the morning and try to get those prescriptions, then," Angel assured me. "Can you give me a printout of that protocol?"

I got her a printout of the Front Line COVID-19 Critical Care Alliance protocol and handed it to her so she could remember the names of the meds and all the protocol details if she needed it the next day.

As I clocked out of my shift and began heading home, they gave Angel her second dose of Remdesivir.

The next night, I returned to work and went to check on Angel. She was now requiring four liters of oxygen via nasal cannula. The curtain on her door was pulled shut, just as tight as it could be. Normally, we only allowed this for people who wanted privacy and were stable enough to somewhat take care of themselves. Otherwise, those glass walls were necessary for us to keep an eye on things.

The lights in her room were turned off, making it a little hard to see. The only source came from the monitor, with a small stream of light coming down from the bathroom sink next to the toilet in the room.

"Are you awake in here?" I whispered, my head just peeking in enough for her to hear me.

"Yeah, I am," she muttered, motioning for me to come in.

She again sat on the edge of the bed. Normally, at this stage, we would've had her lying face down in bed, but because of her body composition, she physically couldn't do that.

"I know they've got the curtain pulled to give you privacy, but you have to call us if you need to get up to use the bathroom," I requested, caringly but stern.

I knew she was the kind of person who would not call for help because she didn't want to bother us but being hooked up to the monitor with all of its chords, she was a high fall risk. She was much sicker now.

"Jodi, I really want to try the Ivermectin," she said to me.

As soon as she said that, I started advocating for her with no time to waste. I went to her nurse and asked her if she knew about Ivermectin. She told me she had heard of it but never researched it, so she didn't know much about early treatment. I directed her to the FLCCC website and told her to research the protocol to make sure it wasn't contraindicated for her. She came back to me and agreed we should try it for Angel.

Then, she called me and said the hospitalist would not prescribe it because it was controversial. So, as hospital supervisor, I called the doctor and nurse to my office and respectfully told the doctor, "Being controversial is not a reason not to practice medicine. Would you be willing to look at some studies and protocols?"

She agreed, and I directed her to the FLCCA website. Shortly after this conversation, the nurse called me and said the doctor ordered it, but now the pharmacist refuses to fill it. By sunrise, I had the pharmacist in my office, so we could coordinate the treatment plan that Angel wanted. While I waited for her to arrive, the Lord placed on my heart the need to record our conversation. So I placed my phone on the desk and hit record.

She walked in, mask in place over her mouth and nose, vigorously rubbing what appeared to be antimicrobial gel into her hands, and stood at the door, about ten feet away.

"Hey," I greeted her with a smile. "Did you get the order from Dr. B for Ivermectin?"

"Not allowed in this facility," she said rather firmly. "Its use is restricted to scabies and lice."

"So physicians can't prescribe off-label medication use here?" I asked as she shook her head no.

"Not for COVID. They did it with hydroxychloroquine, and it was really bad (referring to the flawed study that had been redacted over a year ago), so they're not allowing it right now. If they have an issue with it, they can go to P and T."

"Who is that?" I asked. "Because I have to put it in my house report about the patient advocate kind of thing."

"Who wants it?" she asked.

"Angel."

"The patient wants it?"

"Yeah," I shot back.

The pharmacist took a deep breath and shrugged.

I continued, "I mean, you know when she had talked about, like, everything else is emergency use authorization . . ."

She interrupted, "There's no EUA on Ivermectin."

"Right, right, but . . ."

"It's totally different. Remdesivir is now an official drug."

"Yeah, right, that's not been shown to do anything," I giggled a little, trying to release the tension rising in the room. "But anyway, this is one of our own who wants it. She wants to have it. Her family wants her to have it. So her doctor and nurse printed out information about this treatment, and the doctor agreed to write the script for it. She's not contraindicated."

"I can't . . .I'm not gonna get in the middle of it," she replied emphatically. "If they want it, they need to go through P and T. If they have questions, they can speak to pharmacists on the day shift."

"So I'll just say they need to go to P and T?"

"Yeah, that's the Pharmacy and Therapeutics Committee. There are doctors and pharmacists, and I think there's nursing on that committee. I don't know. I just read the minutes. I don't pay attention to who the people are on it," she smiled. "And if they have questions, they can follow up with the pharmacy on day shift. But on the night shift, we have to follow the formulary."

I was shocked, sad, angry, and scared when I discovered that the pharmacy had blocked this order. Nevertheless, God laid it on my heart to record it, and so I did, not knowing what would happen with it at this point, but I am glad I captured it. This was to be the first of my recordings.

Our conversation continued. "The formulary says it's only approved for these two things. It does not have an EUA. Therefore, it cannot be used here."

"Even if it shows no contraindication to anything she's taking?" I asked again, hoping for a different answer somehow.

Again she replied, "The formulary says I can only use it for lice and scabies."

"Wow, that's sad."

"I am stuck. I'm told, "You are absolutely not to use it under any circumstances whatsoever with anybody with COVID unless you don't want to have a job." If I try to dispense for COVID, I will lose my job. I am not going to lose my job over this. Okay?"

I felt so bad for Angel. This wasn't right. She was looking worse and worse and worse. And it was so sad. I knew she was afraid because she'd lost so many family members in this "pandemic." And I wanted so badly to be an advocate and accomplish her wishes for her.

I tried imploring the pharmacist's sense of advocacy. "We have a chance here to advocate for patients."

"I don't want anything to happen to her," the pharmacist assured me. "I want you to know that my concern is that she is okay. But I have no control over this right now. So you're putting me in a really hard spot."

"Have you researched it? I'm just saying that if you're interested in listening to what some doctors and intensivists worldwide say, do your own research and develop your own opinion."

But she wasn't willing to budge. Her orders came from her supervisors, and she listened to the studies they cited. She said she didn't have time to research. Later that night, Angel sent me a text.

"I heard you were advocating for me. Thank you."

"We're doing everything we can."

The crazy thing is, I wasn't even supposed to be there that night. I was filling in for someone else as house supervisor. Funny how God puts us in the right place at the right time, isn't it?

Monday, I returned to check on Angel again. The room was pitch black, and she was just sitting there, quiet. She wasn't talking much anymore. At this point, she was on Vapotherm®, a type of respiratory support that provides high-velocity oxygen therapy. Basically, she went from having no oxygen the first two days to being on four liters on day three to being on max oxygen when I saw her again less than twenty-four hours later. Even with the extra oxygen supply to her blood, her breathing was poor, and she was struggling. I had to really look her in the eyes to make sure she was hearing and understanding what I was saying.

As I sat there, staring into her eyes, an overwhelming feeling washed over my body, telling me she wasn't going to survive this. "Angel, do you believe in Jesus?" I asked her. I genuinely wasn't sure how she would reply to this. While she was spiritual, we had never directly talked about her belief in Jesus. All I knew was that she held traditional beliefs, which was part of the reason she didn't want to take the shot initially.

"Yes," she replied.

"Would you mind if I prayed with you?"

"Please."

I took off my mask and sat on the bed next to her with my hand on her back. And I prayed, "Dear Father God, please be with Angel as she fights this virus in her body. We ask You to give her peace. You already know the future, and we trust that Your will be done. Thank you, Lord, for peace and comfort for my dear friend. In Jesus' holy name, I pray. Amen."

Angel looked at me with gratitude, "Thank you."

"My pleasure." I smiled and squeezed her hand. "I'll be back to check on you later."

Then I got up quickly to leave the room so she wouldn't see the tears rolling down my face. I was distraught and went back to being alone in my office.

Looking back now, I only wish I had asked if she knew Jesus as her Lord and personal savior. At the time, knowing she followed traditional Native American beliefs, I realized it was a really big deal for her to say she knew Jesus and an even bigger deal to allow me to pray for her. Yet today, there is a tiny seed of doubt, and I wish I could've put that doubt to rest and just made sure that she'd confessed her sins and asked the Lord to come into her heart so I would know she was saved and would see her in heaven one day. I don't know if she was or not, but all I can do now is trust that the Lord met her in the last days of her life, and she found her way. It's so important for us to share our faith whenever the opportunity arises.

Chapter Six

Losing Angel

Even though our hospital has an ICU, we don't have an intensivist doctor on staff. Several specialists were contracted to work there, but very few were specialized in critical care. Because of that, patients who needed intubation would be shipped out to a private hospital as they needed a higher level of care. So while we provide ICU care, intubated COVID patients do not stay in our hospital.

They are sent elsewhere as soon as they are intubated, as we do not have a staff pulmonologist. This was their excuse anyway. They could have always consulted with one. Perhaps this is how they kept costs down in this socialist healthcare system but who foots the bill for these private hospital stays? The taxpayers do. That's who.

Likewise, Angel was going to require a higher level of care than what our hospital offered. That morning she ended up needing to be intubated. Another hospital agreed to take her, but they did not have an available ICU bed yet. So they would have to keep her in an ER bay, which is pretty much a holding pattern, where no one is going to really watch over her, at least not like the care she'd receive in ICU.

While they'd obviously answer alarms and address urgent needs like that, an emergent patient would take precedence over a "stable" patient, and Angel was considered stable. The staff pleaded with the doctors to allow us to care for her because the thought of her being placed in a bay did not sit well with us. Thankfully, our hospital decided to keep her until the bed was available.

Then, there was the whole transportation fiasco. At first, we had trouble getting an ambulance as there had to be an RN on board since she was intubated. This made zero sense to me that paramedics can intubate a patient but cannot transfer one. The stupid things we would do in the name of COVID were unbearable. Time kept ticking by, so finally, I asked if I could be the RN on the transport to facilitate the transfer.

It was settled. I would be the RN to ride with her in the ambulance with a paramedic to facilitate transfer to the other hospital. In the end, though, an RN was able to come. But this RN and the EMT who came with her were not competent. So it was kind of a shit show in her room as they prepared her to leave.

There were two hospital respiratory therapists in Angel's room, the RN and EMT from the ambulance company, and two other nurses from the floor. Unfortunately, they missed a step as they tried to set up their portable ventilator, unhooking her from our hospital ventilator and connecting her to theirs.

"Her oxygen levels are plummeting!" I heard someone in the room call out.

"Recheck the connections," I heard another say.

"It's not working."

"I got it. I got it."

As they were stabilizing her to go, the ambulance RN was having second thoughts, "I don't feel comfortable. I don't feel comfortable."

"Well, I feel comfortable," I piped up. "Let's go." I looked at my hospital peers, "Do you guys agree? Are you okay with us leaving right now? Because if something were to happen, I could bag her while we're driving. And she would have two RNs working on her. You know?"

And everybody was like, "Yeah, I agree. Jodi, you go with her."

It went by without a hitch. Her ride was totally uneventful. I sat in the back of the ambulance next to Angel while the RN was charting.

When we got to the receiving hospital, we were greeted by an entire team of nurses and respiratory therapists who admitted her. As the nurses gowned up to go into Angel's room, I noticed that they were reaching into brown paper bags to retrieve their N95 Masks.

"You guys have to save your masks?" I asked one of the nurses disgustedly.

"Yeah. We don't really have to, but we're keeping up with it."

"Why?" I asked in surprise.

"I have extras, but…"

"At this point? Wow!"

"We don't use the same one every day, but…"

"I know, but, gosh. Aren't we far enough into this to have the needed supplies?" I asked.

"I think we just go into our patient's room a million times a night and go through masks quickly."

"Yeah, it goes against everything we've ever been taught. Huh?" I asked.

"Yep," she replied.

It had been a year and a half since the pandemic started, and still, these nurses were functioning daily by reusing PPE. So after they went into an isolation room ("a million times"), they took off the contaminated mask and put it in the brown paper bag. And then, when they needed to go back into the room, they would take that same contaminated mask, put it back on their face, and reuse it. It was moronic that educated people thought this was a better option than not using one at all.

Another nurse chimed in, "We had a neurosurgeon make a respirator that was way better than this, but administration made us stop using it because it wasn't approved."

"Well, these masks aren't rated for COVID either," I said. She looked at me dumbfounded. "Read what that mask filters," I continued, pointing to the N95 box, "and then research the size of the Coronavirus."

It was mind-blowing that I had to say the same thing hundreds of times to medical professionals.

As the nurses entered the room with Angel, I stood outside the glass windows, watching them assess her and transfer her to their ventilator. Finally, two doctors walked up to the room, stood next to me, and we talked with each other about Angel.

"I mean, look at her," one doctor said.

"I know," replied the other.

"There's another one that's not going to make it."

"It's really sad," I chimed in. "She had just come back from surgery leave a little over two weeks ago when she got her first dose of vaccine after surviving this entire pandemic. And then came into the hospital on Friday room air. . . Sunday, four liters (of oxygen), then maxed out on Vapotherm®, and Intubated today."

The second doctor turned to me and said, "God hates Haiti, Mississippi, Flagstaff, trailer parks, and fat people."

I nervously laughed a little, taken aback by his remarks, "Isn't that what we see mostly, huh? Obese, diabetic, hypertension. . . and the natives are just getting hammered with it."

"Is she Native?" the doctor asked.

"Navajo. She's lost a lot of family members with the handling of this pandemic."

Once she was settled in, I returned to the ambulance for my ride back to my hospital. The ambulance RN greeted me.

"Even though the patient isn't here anymore, this is still considered a COVID ambulance," she said to me. "So you'll need to put your N95 mask back on."

"The patient isn't here anymore."

"Yeah, but she's a COVID patient. So we must gown up because it could be in the air."

"Really?" I was astonished. "You know, she was intubated and on a closed circuit system, right?" I asked. "I'm not putting a mask back on. I'm good."

"Yeah, I know. And we'll spend the next hour cleaning it from top to bottom."

"What? Are you kidding me? She stayed on the gurney and on a ventilator the entire time. It's not transmitted by contact. It's airborne."

"I know, but it's what we've gotta do. We have to follow the rules. That's the policy."

"Well, you go ahead and wipe it down. I agree with that."

"And then we're going to let it air out for an hour."

"You're just going to sit this rig out with the door open for an hour and just chill?"

"Yup."

"While patients are waiting to be transported?"

"Yeah, it's protocol."

"That's the problem. Nobody is using common sense," I shot back.

"Well, it doesn't really hurt."

"Yes, it does. It hurts all kinds of patients that need transport to a higher level of care. While you air this thing out, they're waiting and not getting the treatment they need. All this so we can do things that look good on paper but make no sense, and people suffer!"

A couple of days after Angel was transferred, I came back to work in the ICU. Shortly after my arrival, I was approached by another nurse.

"Hey, Jodi, I'm going to be heading out for lunch. Can

you take report? I just have a fifteen-year-old who's got double pulmonary embolisms."

Confused, I stood there for a moment. We don't have a pediatric floor or a pediatrician. I was shocked they didn't transfer him out to Phoenix Children's ospital. A pulmonary embolism is a serious condition and occurs when something, typically a blood clot, blocks the large arteries in either of your lungs, and this poor kid had it happen in each of his lungs. What was more concerning was that he seemed awfully young to have such intense lung problems. I figured he surely must have had some other medical issues that would have led him here this early in life.

"Fifteen?" I asked, still taken aback by the situation. "Is he overweight and sedentary?"

"No, perfectly healthy weight and an athlete."

"Is he a diabetic?" I asked, grasping at straws.

"Nah."

"Is he vaccinated for COVID?"

"I don't know," she said as she walked past me, heading towards the elevators to leave.

"How does she not know if he was vaccinated?" I thought to myself. "This is highly unusual. She should have done some critical thinking and research."

While she was on her break, I decided to go through the patient's file just to get a better picture of what I was dealing with in case something emergent happened. I found out that he was not only vaccinated but had been only two weeks prior, and now he's lying in a hospital bed with blood clots. I reviewed the progress notes from the hospitalist, and not one of them addressed that he had recently gotten the COVID vaccination, instead just commenting on how odd of a condition it was for somebody his age.

Suddenly, alarms began to go off in my head. After seeing my friend denied her request for Ivermectin and hydroxychloroquine, and now seeing the blatant denial of the mere possibility that people could be suffering side effects from vaccines, I was growing increasingly wary of the direction this was headed. So I pulled out my phone and took a picture of the file and the doctor's notes.

On another shift, I was stationed in the ER. Another nurse approached me and gave me the report of a thirty-something-year-old patient we had in room eight. He had a slight cough on Tuesday, and by Saturday, he was struggling to breathe. Once again, he had been vaccinated for COVID-19 just two weeks prior and received his second shot, you guessed it, on Tuesday, the day he developed a cough.

I approached the doctor who was on at that time. "Hey, Doc. Did you see eight's lab results? Is he in a cytokine storm?" (Note: This is when an infection triggers your immune system to flood your bloodstream with inflammatory proteins called cytokines. They can kill tissue and damage your organs.)

"Well. . ." he looked at the chart. "He's COVID-negative," he paused in deep thought. His face looked as though he were puzzled. "You know. This isn't making sense. He tested positive for COVID last year, and he's vaccinated, but his COVID test is negative."

"Could it be vaccine related?" I asked, already knowing the answer, "because he just got his second dose on Tuesday and developed a cough."

"Oh."

That's when another doctor approached and added her two cents to the conversation. I was shocked! Throughout this entire time, she sat quietly at her desk, always gloved and masked.

"The problem is that they are not doing studies."

"It's not that it hasn't been done. It hasn't been published," replied the first doctor.

"How come, after all these months, we haven't had any

research? Isn't that fishy to you?" I asked him.

The second doctor went on. "It probably hasn't been done because the government doesn't want to show that the darn vaccine is full of sh@t." (Meaning, it's not doing what it was created to do).

A while later, doctor one went off shift, and doctor two took over the patient's care. We resumed our conversation.

"Now, you've got this guy who got his second dose of vaccine and developed a cough. His BMP is elevated, all his liver enzymes are elevated . . ."

"He's probably got myocarditis," the doctor quipped back. "Yes!"

"Oh, this is bullsh@t," she said angrily. "Now, myocarditis probably due to the vaccine!"

"Right," I agreed.

"They're not going to blame the vaccine," she said.

"But he has an obligation to report that, doesn't he?" The doctor nodded her head 'yes'. "It happened. What is it, up to sixty days after, if you see anything, you're supposed to report it, right?" I asked.

"They have got to."

"But how many people are reporting?" I asked.

"They are not reporting," the doctor admonished. "Because they want to shove it under the mat."

The CDC mandated reporting adverse effects such as this, but it wasn't happening. I saw dozens of people come in with adverse reactions to the vaccine, but there were always excuses for not reporting these safety signals. One of the major reasons was that our hospital never released guidance on what to look out for and report before or during the mass vaccination. It also takes at least thirty uninterrupted minutes to complete this burdensome, detailed report. And if you had to walk away from your computer, it would time out, and you'd have to start all over.

I kept up with Angel's status. Sadly, she passed away two weeks after being transferred. I was saddened, yes, but ultimately I had righteous anger that we did not honor her right to autonomy and uphold our ethical principles to do no harm. I had already made peace with knowing she wasn't going to survive since the Lord laid it on my heart in her hospital room. She was such a sweet person, despite her humanity and the things that she had suffered here on earth. The Lord decided it was time for her to pass on. I believe that He knew that her situation would light a fire under me to sound the alarm and become a whistleblower. After all, her story is the reason I decided to come forward.

A few days later, I was with the hospital supervisor, and Angel's aunt called in to call off work the next day. I said to her," I'm not sure if you know, but I was the one who transported her to the other hospital."

"Thank you for that," her kindness was felt through the phone.

I was so emotional tears began streaming down my cheeks. "We prayed together," I told her, wanting her to know she had done that before she was intubated.

"Her mom is having a really hard time. But we are thankful for you being there with her and helping her."

When I got off the phone, I reflected on sitting next to Angel and praying with her. All I could think was, "I hope that I told her to ask for her sins to be forgiven." I began to cry more and more. I just remember sitting next to her and thinking, "This is it. He's taking her."

I vowed right then and there, "Her death won't be in vain. The world will know that there are alternative treatments and that pharmacists are being weaponized to block doctors' orders, interfering with the physician-patient relationship. They'll know that there were so many adverse events occurring with this so-called vaccine."

Every now and again, when I think of her, it just hits me,

and I sob. It happens at the craziest times. One minute I think I'm fine, and the next, I break down crying uncontrollably. It's overwhelming.

Wow. I can't believe this is the path for my life.

Chapter Seven

North to Alaska

After successfully recording the pharmacist who denied Angel the order written by the doctor, I started recording more and more. At first, I recorded just for myself. I didn't want to walk away from a conversation about a colleague I cared about without being sure that my accuracy was true and not affected by the emotions of the situation. I was convinced that my understanding was correct when I listened to it. She was simply "following orders."

From that point on, I decided I would record every time the situation would call for it. I have recordings of me doing my rounds to get updates on all the inpatients from the on-duty nurses for my house report to the oncoming hospital supervisor. On many occasions, they'd tell me somebody was labeled as COVID-positive, even though they were not being treated for COVID. One day, there was a patient in for GI issues, another for an abdominal wound, a pregnant patient who needed her gallbladder out, and several more. All I knew was that story after story began to present itself to me very quickly. So once I collected several videos, I sent them over to Chloe at Project Veritas, saying, "Here's my story."

Very quickly, almost from the second I hit submit, I began second-guessing myself. "Yikes! What in the world did I just do?"

I wondered silently. My heart began to race as questions pulsed rapid fire through my mind because I honestly didn't know.

- Is that there for them to do whatever they want with it now?
- When are they going to talk to me?
- Where are they going to talk to me?
- Can I trust them?
- Are they just going to take this stuff I've sent and expose it?
- Do I have any input into how it's presented?

On one hand, I was freaking out inside, but on the other, I was extremely relieved that the reality and gravity of this "pandemic" were out. People were finally going to know, and they were going to see what was happening in our hospitals.

Days after sending the video, Chloe reached out to me, saying that Project Veritas would love to fly me out to their headquarters and interview me.

"I'd love to," I replied. "But I'm leaving for Alaska to spend a couple of weeks with my son for his thirtieth birthday. Can I come after that?" I had a huge trip planned, and COVID had already taken so much from us. We needed this trip. Chloe and I settled on the particulars, and it was official. Project Veritas was going to expose it to the world!

After getting this news, I talked to a couple of the doctors I trusted and asked them to come on board with me. They said they appreciated what I was doing and supported me, but they weren't as brave or courageous as I was.

This kind of irritated me. To me, this wasn't about being brave or having the courage to stand in the face of opposition. We were violating our ethical principles. As healthcare professionals, we took an oath to do no harm (among others). So to watch my fellow nurses and doctors sit back, and let this immoral system kill people was tearing me apart.

Next, I sat down with my three kids to explain the situation. "Listen, you guys know how I feel about COVID and the handling of it," I told them. "I recorded some of the situations and conversations I've had at work and sent them to Project Veritas. They're going to blow the whistle on this whole thing."

"Mom, we know that if this is what you feel like God is telling you to do, then you absolutely need to follow through with it," my oldest son replied.

Throughout all of this, my family was supportive. I think I developed some credibility with them from the beginning, as the entire time, I had been explaining to them what was happening at work and the research I'd been doing. They saw how I was living my life as normal as possible, even with all the COVID narrative going on. And my oldest was working at an ER in our area, one of the largest in the nation. So we'd spend time hanging out and exchanging stories of what was going on, especially ones that contrasted the narrative the media had been pushing. We both saw a lot of mental health patients come through our hospitals, but they were nowhere near overwhelmed.

My daughter, however, was concerned. "What happens if you go to jail from the videos, mom?"

"Honey, I don't even care," I said, letting slip some of the exhaustion and frustration I'd been feeling. "I mean, at this point, we're talking about people's lives. I don't just mean their physical lives but their mental and spiritual health, too. They're so brainwashed they don't know what to believe. They need to see what's actually happening. You guys have had me telling you what's really going on, but most of these people only hear what the media and our politicians are telling them. Somebody needs to step up and let people see behind the curtain, even if they don't like it."

My daughter begged me to at least call and ask an attorney what could happen to me, and I promised I would, even though it didn't matter what they said. Unfortunately, he was busy when

I called, so his paralegal answered instead. "Listen, I'm a federal employee, and I have some recordings I took in the hospital. This deals with patient safety and public health, so I want to expose it."

"All I can tell you is that Arizona is a one-party consent state, so you can record anybody without their knowledge, and there's nothing they can do about it."

"Well, that's good enough for me." Truthfully, even if it was illegal, I would've done it. Too many lives were at stake to care about mine.

The trip to Alaska was amazing! Spending two weeks with my firstborn alone exploring the "Last Frontier" together was priceless. Sometimes overwhelming thoughts would come into my head like a panic attack, but he would always comfort me and calm me down. It was awe-inspiring to see the man he had become, and I wouldn't have wanted to be with anyone else during that time. He was so confident and at peace with all of it, telling me he was proud of me. Never once did he ever express anything resembling fear or concern. He only talked about it if I brought it up, which I tried really hard not to do. He and I are super close. We practically grew up together since I had him when I was sixteen years old and was a single mom. I was stoked to be able to take him on this trip of a lifetime and spend quality time, just the two of us, adventuring. We went dog sledding, white water rafting, deep sea fishing, glacier climbing, and so much more. It was magical and the last state he needed to go to complete all fifty.

While there, I was working remotely with Chloe, developing the story for Project Veritas. She had a love for the Lord like me. This really helped me loosen up a little as I became increasingly more comfortable talking with her about something so vulnerable to me. It was almost like when I sent over those videos, the weight of the world was lifted off of my shoulders. Now, people would get to see things for themselves. Then, they could make their own decisions. All I needed was to give people a chance to witness the reality taking place in the hospital and decide for themselves what was true.

On our fishing trip, we met a surgeon, his wife, and another nurse and her son. Because it was something that was such a large part of our lives and something we could all easily relate to, the topic of COVID obviously came up. Everyone felt the same way my son and I did, which gave me a lot of comfort. Knowing that other people like me were not afraid to speak up and fight against the hoard of mindless sheep simply following orders gave me a boost of confidence that I was doing the right thing. I told them to keep their eyes open and that something big was coming to help change the fight against COVID.

After this, I kept getting those feelings of strength and comfort. I'd look around at all of God's glory in this magnificent place, spending time in prayer and asking Him to lead me.

When I was about to head home, Chloe called to say she was flying me out to San Antonio that Sunday. So I flew home with little time to rest before hopping onto a plane to Texas.

Chapter Eight

Code Name Scorpion

My plane landed in San Antonio, and I went outside to the arriving passengers' transportation area, where I saw a man standing with a sign that read, "SCORPION." After a minute, my phone vibrated with a text from Chloe. "By the way, you're getting picked up by a driver, and they're not going to use your real name. Instead, we're using your code name, so keep an eye out for Scorpion." This was a pretty funny coincidence to me. I don't read or follow my daily horoscope, but my astrology sign is Scorpio, and what I was exposing would send a sting to this COVID operation.

It was a charming little city, but it had a very odd, evil vibe surrounding the hotel, which I wouldn't notice until later that evening while walking with Chloe to find somewhere to eat. There were people on the streets high as a kite and in a world of their own. Homeless people gathered together on almost every block we turned, and there were small groups of people looking shifty. Being raised in Chicago, I have a keen sense of street smarts, so I could tell they were looking for trouble.

Pulling into the hotel driveway, the first thing I noticed was just how beautiful the building was. It was an old historic hotel right in the heart of downtown, overlooking a park. When I walked in through the front doors, I was overcome with a luscious smell that was so amazing it penetrated my senses. Right away, I could tell that Project Veritas was a legit organization and was going to take good care of me.

This place was gorgeous. From the grayish blue decor with pops of yellow to the wooden chairs that appeared to be luxury antiques, I was super comfy from the start. I'm well-traveled, but to visit as many places as I do, I tend to save money on hotels and stay at hostels, so this was luxurious to me.

At the front desk, I checked in with my code name, Scorpion. It makes me laugh every time I write it as if I was in a James Bond movie and I was a supporting character.

Chloe instructed me to order room service if I needed anything and to take the time to relax in my room since it would be a couple of hours before I would meet with James or the team.

When I finally got up to the room with the team, I was extremely nervous but with a "let's do this" type of attitude!

I entered a foyer with a tall circular table filled with water bottles, takeout food, and snacks with an opulent chandelier above it and all kinds of people standing around. Ahead of me was a formal dining room. It was rectangular in shape and had ten or so people seated around it. These included those from the production team to the journalists, lawyers, and investigators. To the left of that table was the living room, also lengthy in shape with several bright lights and cameras lined up. This is where I would do the interview. They then started showing me the video and how they had edited the clips altogether.

While we were discussing the videos, James walked into the room, stretched out his hand, and introduced himself. "Hi, I'm James O'Keefe."

I shook his hand, "Hi, James. It's very nice to meet you. I'm Jodi."

"Listen, Jodi. We need to get the pharmaceutical companies and take them down," he said.

"Honestly, James, I'm right there with you. There's

something nefarious going on here. The thing is, James, people are brainwashed. They don't think critically or listen to facts. The only thing they've heard for months is, "You're helping society, and if you don't wear your mask, you'll kill grandma." We need to hit them on an emotional level. Nothing else will do. We can spread facts all day long, but unless we tap into their emotions, I don't think we will have a breakthrough."

He smiled as he hurried past in his workout clothes. "I'll see you in a couple of hours for the interview," he said, brushing off my statement as he disappeared into the bedroom.

I could only chuckle and wonder if he had seen the videos yet.

After this, I went up to the rooftop with Chloe. The two of us were there alone, just talking and passing time. I requested a cocktail to calm my nerves. Chloe is a spitfire! She's a "say what you mean, mean what you say" type of gal. Her family fled communism, and she didn't like the direction our country was headed. So, she decided to do something about it and began working with Project Veritas.

While we were up there, we prayed that God would guide this whole interview. That He would let the story flow as it should and get into people's hearts and minds. I also personally asked Him to speak through me and to guard my heart, mind, and tongue. I ask this of Him often.

After a little while, one of the production crew comes out, and Chloe walks away to talk with him. I couldn't hear what they were saying, but it was clearly a passionate discussion because both of them got pretty animated.

As she walked back, I heard her say, "I told them! I've been trying to tell them!" Then, she sat back down and looked at me.

"What was that all about?" I asked.

"Jodi, they're only just now realizing what they've got in their hands," she said with a grin.

"Really, they had no idea what I actually recorded? It took

them this long?" I asked with a smile.

"Yeah, I've been talking to them. They were actually going to pass up the story. We have a team of people that go through the emails we get, and they didn't pay much attention to yours. So one night, I was going through the emails because I like to help. Small team and all, y'know? Comparatively, for fighting all this evil, it's not some huge corporation we have. It's closer to a family. Anyways, I eventually found yours. That was when I realized that you had something big, and I told them I would reach out to you."

"After meeting with you and talking it over, they're only now realizing the gravity of the videos you sent in." We both laughed. It seemed like God was already moving our story along. I wasn't upset. After all, there aren't many organizations willing to expose corruption, and the days of investigative journalism are fading. Project Veritas receives thousands of emails weekly, and they don't have hundreds of employees.

After some more talking, I realized it was almost time for the interview to start. The interview was supposed to start at five but didn't get underway until eight o'clock that night.

"Chloe, before I start the interview, I want to pray with the entire team. Can you tell them that?"

Admittedly, I was extremely nervous. After so much time, with so much corruption uncovered, it all came to this moment. I am not a public speaker, so I feared I'd mess this up. The story would be dead with it, and my only hope of spreading this message would quickly be gone. "I'd like to pray as a team."

"Jodi, I'm not sure that's such a good idea..." Chloe wasn't aware of what everyone's religious beliefs were and how they would take to the idea.

"Listen, Chloe, we need to pray before we start this interview. That's what we need to do," I insisted. Before we departed, she and I stood up and held hands as she prayed a simple prayer, asking God for guidance and strength to make it through this challenge. Chloe was my sister in Christ.

Right before the interview, I returned to my hotel room to gather my thoughts. My spirit was heavy. I fell to my knees beside the bed and prayed out loud, "Father, what is it you want me to say and do?" I asked, crying with anguish.

The weeks leading up to this were filled with many moments of peace as well as rushing feelings of panic that would paralyze me in my tracks. I would have to constantly remind myself that Yahweh is not the creator of confusion, Satan is. Our Father would never lay something on our heart to do and then cause anxiety. That is the work of Satan.

As I walked back into the penthouse room where everyone else was waiting, the only thing I could focus on was the blinding lights and the massive cameras. Everybody was running around, rushing 'til the last minute to ensure everything would run smoothly. To my surprise, it took us a couple more hours of setup before we would begin, giving me time to get my camera-ready makeup done. This, too, gave me anxiety. I rarely wear makeup, and the few times I have had it professionally applied, I felt it changed my appearance too much. I made sure to stress the importance of looking as natural as possible, which is an oxymoron with layers of makeup donning my face.

Right before we started filming, I stood up and said, "I would like everyone to stop what they're doing and pray with me. I'm only here because I was led to do this, and this is very scary. I don't know what's going to come of this, but I want to make sure it's God's hand guiding it." I had contemplated not doing it because I was so nervous I didn't want to add to it, but the dark forces of anxiety and fear were penetrating me, and the only way to combat that was to ask the Holy Ghost to take over.

James stood up, and they all gathered around, and we prayed together. As soon as he sat back down, the cameras immediately started rolling. Outside of our initial meeting, James and I didn't talk about how the interview would go or the questions he was going to ask. He just asked with a comforting tone and smile, "Are you ready to do this?"

I was sitting directly across from James in a gray leather chair, wearing my long sleeve navy blue shirt. On one sleeve, it says, "Intensive Care," and on the other, "Emergency." On the back was a large cross with "RN." A Navajo woman to whom I had administered chemotherapy (she later passed away) made the brightly colored beaded necklace on which my employee badge hung. On my wrist was a beaded native bracelet given to me by a Navajo CNA I worked with. Parallel to our chairs was a large screen television where we would intermittently refer to video footage between James' questions.

"My name is Jodi O'Malley, and I am a master's prepared Registered Nurse," I said, introducing myself. "I work for Health and Human Services under the Indian Health Services branch for the Native Americans."

After the first clip played, James looked me in the eye and sternly asked, "Tell us about who this person is."

Here we go, I thought to myself as I stared at my coworker on the screen.

When we got to a clip of me transferring Angel to the other hospital, I felt a lot of emotions welling up inside of me.

"So, what are we looking at here?" James asked.

"You're looking at me," my voice began to break up with emotion, then I pulled it back together. "...transferring her to a higher level of care that could handle her condition."

As his questions continued, so did the escalation of my emotions. I was overcome. "Don't cry," I quietly commanded myself. "Don't cry!" Everything that had happened for the past eighteen months had led me to this moment, and the emotion of it all was rushing through my veins like a tsunami.

The interview continued on. Finally, as we neared the end, I said, "Right now, what is plaguing this country is the spirit of fear."

"Why are you choosing to blow the whistle?" James asked. "It's not what a lot of people would do. They're scared. They're afraid. Are you afraid?"

I replied, "It's my career, you know? It's how I help people. But am I afraid? I wouldn't necessarily say I am afraid because my faith lies in God and not man. I have two older kids that are on their own. And I have an eleven-year-old at home who I care for on my own. What kind of person would I be if I knew all of this...? This is evil. This is evil at the highest level. You have the FDA, you have the CDC, that are both supposed to be protecting us, but they are under the government, and everything that we've done so far is unscientific."

"Are you afraid they are going to retaliate against you?"

"Yeah. I'm a federal employee," I said with increasing boldness. "What other federal employees do you see coming out?"

"But you put your faith in God."

"Amen."

During the entire interview, I was trembling inside. It was one of the most nerve-wracking experiences of my entire life. The whole time, all I could think was, "What am I going to say? Did I say that right? Am I doing the right thing here?" The enemy loves to attack the hardest when you are on the path to doing good, and boy, was he present that day. It was so hard for me to find the words.

The next day, one of the production crew came up to me while I was sitting with Chloe. "Jodi, thank you for starting off with a prayer last night. I was really moved by your story and what you're doing. You're a hero. You're going to change this narrative, Jodi. I just want to tell you that my faith has kinda been shaky over the last couple of years because of everything happening in the world. I haven't been as close to God as I should be lately. But when you came in, and you stood boldly on your faith, your beliefs, your conviction... with what you've done, and how you're doing it—praying for all of us. . . I really needed that. You inspired me to do the same. I'm going to lean on God and talk to Him. Thank you."

"YES!" I thought sharing Jesus with the world was what this journey on earth was about! That was such a big thing for me to hear. When you step out from amongst the crowd, you never know for certain that it will help people. And sometimes, it can be a long while before you see any fruit. But this time, the Lord sent me feedback immediately to let me know I was already making a difference. And it wasn't even anything I would've anticipated, like a production member being touched by my faith to cling back to his.

"Wow!" Chloe said, "God is moving, Jodi. What you have done is going to change things."

My tears flowed like a river. While I never doubted I was on the right path, sometimes things can become hard to handle, and the pressure of your mission can be overwhelming. But just hearing that, I found a new sense of vigor to keep pressing forward. She was right. His Spirit was moving.

One thing that pleasantly surprised me was just how many Christians were on the Project Veritas team. James, for instance, is an awesome guy. He's been fighting evil for a long time now. Still, I think having my story come around and having me speak boldly in Jesus' name inspired him a lot, too. Later, he told me that he uses my "fear God, not man" line all the time.

After the interview, I told him, "James, you've got a lot of angels around you. I don't know if you really realize it, but God's gathering His people, and I think He's gathering them for a time like this."

It was amazing to be a part of this experience but also humbling to think I was chosen to do this. As the scripture says, Jesus knew us before the foundation of the world. I mean, sure, that's obvious. He's the beginning and the end, right? So He knows it all, but I am humbled to see it in action and that the

Lord chose me to facilitate His will.

Chapter Nine

Blowing the Whistle

About two weeks after I recorded the interview, I received a phone call. "Hey, Jodi, It's Chloe. Our team just finished the editing, and the video's going live soon. We want to fly you out to our Miami location, so you can be here when it airs."

A hurricane had blown through and destroyed their office in New York only weeks earlier, so they traveled from state to state, doing their stories from hotel to hotel. "That would be great. There's just one thing. I need to bring my youngest son. I've been gone with my oldest for two weeks. Plus, our lives are going to completely change after this, and I want him to experience it with me." Without hesitation, they agreed.

Before they flew us out that Monday, I had the weekend to celebrate with some of my girlfriends, Jessica and Molly. Molly is a hospice worker, and Jessica is a social worker. They share a servant's heart with me and were always available for me to vent my frustrations. Through that, they could understand the pain I was experiencing, watching the corruption unfold, lining pockets at the expense of medical freedom and lives. We had hung out a lot during COVID, and they were there during some of the hardest parts.

During the height of the pandemic, when it was difficult to even find a place where you could sit down, we wound up going to a cigar bar which was one of the few places where we could relax and be comfortable without wearing a mask. It was a slice of normalcy in a world that had become consumed by fear. From our frequent visits, we got to know some of the staff and regular patrons pretty well. We had amazing conversations, and Jessica started dating one of the managers, too. It was a whirlwind romance kind of deal, and now they were getting married.

I decided to spend the weekend with these friends as she hosted her bachelorette party at a spa in north Scottsdale. I wanted this weekend to be about my friend and her wedding and the beautiful story that it was. I shared some information about what was going on but kept it brief to avoid drawing attention away from her celebration. They were all very supportive. All, except one, who holds a very left-leaning ideology. She was trying to wrap her head around the whole concept of it, didn't say much, and still was kind and loving to me.

On Sunday, after I departed from them, I got this feeling that something was wrong and that I should fly out that night instead of waiting until the next morning as planned. I've learned to allow the Holy Spirit to lead and myself to be led, so I called Project Veritas. "Hey guys, I have a feeling I need to get out of this suite today. So, book me on this flight, and let me head over."

Within fifteen minutes, our flight had been changed, and Benjamin and I were on our way to Miami.

Chloe picked us up at the airport and took us to the hotel, where we did our SCORPION check-in and headed off to our room to get some rest. We had a big day ahead of us.

Benjamin and I did our best to have a little fun the next day while we waited for the big moment that would happen that evening. First, we put on our fancy robes and giggled as we snapped several photos of ourselves in them. Then, we spent a little time walking the grounds of the hotel.

It was amazing to have a moment for the two of us to get away, forget about this crazy life, and just spend time together. First, we had lunch and then went for a little beach time. Eventually, evening came, and we made our way to the Project Veritas suite.

Before the story went live, Benjamin and I sat around, talking with some of the Veritas team. While a suite is probably quite large for most folks, the space was a bit crowded with a dozen or so of us.

So, imagine your family members popping in and out of the room, food on the counter —constantly being ordered and delivered and frequently wrong. LOL. The team is mostly guys in their twenties and thirties, so they're always eating while ensuring they get their daily workouts in. They're such a great group of people. I just adored them. They were very open and honest, kind and loving, and they took good care of us.

Everyone was on their laptops, ready to watch things happen in real-time. "Jodi, we were thinking maybe you should set up a GiveSendGo campaign," one of the producers said to me.

Me and my kids had already talked about setting one up before, but I still wasn't entirely convinced I should. After all, I was only doing what I felt I needed to, what God was telling me to do. I just wanted to help people see the corruption that was happening behind closed doors. Why should I be getting paid for this? "I dunno.... Let me make a phone call, and I'll get back to you."

With that, I excused myself and went into the other room. I called my oldest son, JJ, to see what he thought about it. "Hey, you got a second?"

"Sure, Mom, what's up?"

"Listen, they asked me if I set up a GiveSendGo campaign, and I really don't know what to do here."

"Well, Mom, absolutely you should do it," he told me, his serious tone cutting through my doubts. "Listen, you have no idea what's going to happen after this. What if they take away your license, or if you need to hire attorneys? You need to protect yourself, and the only way you can do that is if you have no fear of the rug being pulled out from under you." With that, he started a campaign for me.

The big event we were awaiting was finally here—the official release of my Project Veritas video. It was such a big moment for me. Smiling, I looked over at Benjamin, who sat perched on the side arm of the couch, staring, like the rest of us, at the television screen as the video began to play. The energy in the room was off the charts.

As soon as my story aired, I went out on the balcony to smoke a cigar. LOL. My nerves were shot. Benjamin stayed for a couple of hours but then went to our room. He enjoyed spending time alone and ordering warm milk and cookies from room service. He was reveling in the opulence of it all and likened his experience to the movie *Like Mike,* or *Home Alone.*

Out on the balcony, I looked up to the biggest, most beautiful rainbow in the sky. Chloe and I really connected at that moment. We discussed how God's promises are always true. I realize that the sign of the rainbow was that He wouldn't flood the earth again, but we saw it as the most amazing sign from heaven that we were on the right track. We prayed together again. Chloe and I were always talking to God together.

That night was such a whirlwind. Almost immediately, different team members called out things live as they happened.

"They've already removed the video from Instagram!"

"Hey, #covidvaxexposed is trending on Twitter, and we are banned from Twitter!" they exclaimed.

My son had the GiveSendGo campaign all set up and ready to go in time for the release. He created it in his name and stated all donations would go to me. If I remember correctly, we got about $60,000 in just the first few hours! The overwhelming support people were giving me was absolutely nuts. The stream of comments flowing into my inbox was constant, all from people just as frustrated as us. I read each one with such gratitude.

- Thank you!
- Thank you, I knew something wasn't right.
- Thank you for being brave, for stepping up and speaking out.

Family members called me, saying, "Oh, so and so reached out." I got so much support that night. It was crazy. In fact, I only had one negative comment. It was from a nurse I worked with, "I can't believe you did this to Angel." I replied, "Did what to Angel?" She never again reached out.

In total, I received 15,000 comments, emails, and prayers from people, some of which I still haven't been able to read through. In addition, people were calling me directly, telling me their churches were praying for me, others thanking me, and some were trying to figure out other ways they could support me.

"Do you see?" Chloe asked me. "Do you finally see what you've got here?"

I had a couple of interviews in those early hours. First, Charlie Kirk called, and the next day, I spoke with Alex Jones from InfoWars.

While the PV team told me I would end up talking to Candace Owens and Tucker Carlson, I never heard anything from either of them. The disappointing fact was nobody from the mainstream media reached out to me for an interview. Yet, to this day, there's been radio silence from those in strong positions of power over the media.

I don't hold any judgment toward them. Frankly, I have no idea what their reasons are. I mostly look back and can only think, what a shame it is that more people did not see this and know what was happening.

Chapter Ten

One Last Moment of Normal

A few days later, Benjamin and I went to Chicago for a family wedding. Leaving Miami, the peaceful calm I'd had all along seemed to waiver. It was a scary time. Before, I felt so sheltered and protected from the world, away from the prosecution and persecution awaiting me. Now, my story was out, and my private life seemed to be gone.

I couldn't help but wonder, "What will life look like going forward? How public will I have to be? Was my purpose fulfilled by this exposure? Can I finally have some reprieve?" During these times, I talked to Yeshua (the Hebrew name for Jesus) a lot. I had the same anguish now that I had in June 2020 when I had already grown weary of researching, educating, and sharing in what appeared to be futile efforts trying to influence other nurses to follow our ethical principles and evidence-based practice, the foundation of nursing.

There was nowhere to hide. My life was public now, as was the past that came along with it. Panic-stricken feelings were manifesting in my body with thoughts of what "skeletons" would come out. Did I have skeletons? What were they? Every time I would lift these feelings up to Yeshua, the bold, quiet assuredness of the Holy Ghost would come upon me with the reminder that I have repented of my sins (many times, LOL), and they were forgiven. After all, I follow God, not man, as I would repeat in my interviews.

> *He has not dealt with us according to our sins, Nor punished us according to our iniquities. For as the heavens are high above the earth, So great is His mercy toward those who fear Him; As far as the east is from the west, So far has He removed our transgressions from us.*
>
> *- Psalms 103:10-12*

By the time I was twenty-years-old, I had lived a life most wouldn't experience in their entire lifetime. First, I was a fifteen-year-old high school dropout with a fake ID and a full-time job. By sixteen, I was a mother in a narcissistic, abusive relationship with a man who was fourteen years my senior. By seventeen, I was divorced, and at twenty, I moved out on my own with my six-month-old daughter and three-year-old son. I partied with rock stars, traveled the world, and was always game for adventures. I've lived a life filled with the kind of experiences that romance novels are made of. But the details of that are a story for another time.

When we arrived at the Chicago airport, one of my dear friends, who I've known since I was that fifteen-year-old unhindered and unafraid little girl, picked us up. My son's father picked up Benjamin to hang out with him for a few days. My friend and I went back to the hotel we were staying at so that we could talk.

"Jodi, I am so proud of you. Seeing you stand up and speak

out like that, it's inspiring," she said with tear-filled eyes.

She's six years older than me, so I always kind of looked up to her like an older sister. She had been there for me through a lot of hard times and always seemed to know what to say. So hearing her say she was proud of me made me tear up.

While we had been close for many years, throughout COVID, we started talking less and less. This wasn't uncommon for us. We never had the type of catty relationship that a lot of women have, where one of us gets mad when the other hasn't checked in with the other. Our relationship is unbreakable. She always leaned a little more on the liberal side of the aisle, but that wasn't a problem between us. We continuously show love and mutual respect for one another.

But with the media making every topic polarizing, people were now rabid over this subject. She quietly disappeared from social media, where I was primarily talking to people at the time. Through the chaos of just trying to live my everyday life and take care of patients the best I could while immersing myself in education, we stopped talking for a bit somewhere along the way. It wasn't until I sat in that room that I realized this.

"I've been off social media for months now. I started drawing and journaling to calm my mind. Everything lately just seems to be piling up mentally," my friend said. "Between the lockdowns, not being able to see people I knew, and all the BLM stuff, I just haven't felt safe... So I went out and got my concealed carry permit."

"I just wish I knew. I didn't want to take the vaccine, and I did, Jodi." With tears welling up in her eyes and with bone-chilling emotion, she said, "I did it because everybody was pushing me towards it! They said I needed it to be safe. I just knew in my spirit something was wrong. Am I going to die? Am I going to hell?" She asked me.

I had already received similar questions from other people reaching out to me. Some people believed that the vaccine was the mark of the beast. Others thought they were doomed for living in fear and not trusting God. But to hear this coming from somebody who was basically family worried me. It was painful seeing how tormented she was over her decision.

Throughout the five days we spent together, she kept asking me, "I can't believe I did it. I can't believe I took it. I didn't want to, so why did I take this vaccine?"

And every time, I would reassure her, "Listen, it's not going to affect everybody negatively. There are studies out there, enough to make me believe that your body will be able to handle it because you only got two. But some people just can't. We've known that the spike protein which is transferred in the lipid nanoparticles ends up in an organ, and they get affected by it. Live in the moment, pray, and ask God for forgiveness. You cannot let it affect you like this. That is the work of the enemy (Satan)."

"But Jodi, I feel like I went directly against what God was telling me to do."

"Forgiveness doesn't stop at one mistake. If you're truly repentant, you'll be fine," I assured her.

Throughout the pandemic, I followed a group of experts, some for the entire duration and others for only about six months. One of those people was Tammy Clark, a government-trained OSHA expert who went viral sharing the truth about masks early on in the pandemic. Right after my story broke, I got a message from Tammy. "Welcome to the Whistleblower family. I'm so proud of you! Courage is contagious. If there's anything at all you need from me, feel free to reach out. We're family now." I was so excited to get this message from her!

While in Chicago for my friend's wedding, I learned that Tammy was in town. I needed to see her, probably more than anybody else. I could not wait to meet her and tell her all that she had done for me throughout this time. She and Kristin Meghan were the rocks I could lean on and learn from. They had a plethora of knowledge, and how they presented it captivated me. They never let up on sharing the truth with the world, even when it seemed like nobody was listening.

She picked me up from my hotel, and we went to a bar down the street from my hotel and sat outside. Meeting her for the first time was an incredible experience. She got me, and I got her! It was an immediate kindred connection. I caught her up on everything that had been going on and the worries that I'd been feeling. She told me, "Jodi, courage is contagious. You just continue to let God guide you, lead you, and speak the truth through you."

Sitting there, I realized I had cultivated relationships with new best friends. Even today, when I share something on Facebook from a memory, I tell them, "See guys? I knew we were going to be friends. I was creeping on you before we even met!"

She filled me in on what I could expect from being a whistleblower now. "These days, you cannot believe what you see or hear. It is only the peace that comes from the Holy Spirit that you will know if you are following good or evil. In the last days, confusion and chaos will abound." I knew what she was talking about.

As a woman who is a follower of Jesus, her spiritual advice was well received. These days I have a hard time calling myself Christian since the vast majority don't represent His teachings very well. Many allowed fear to penetrate their soul, afraid to gather and worship while strip clubs and football games were happening all around them. They separated themselves from their family based on vaccination status. I don't belong to a particular church but I do gather with other followers of Yeshua and listen to sermons regularly.

Then, Tammy dropped me off at the wedding, and we had a beautiful moment praying together and being so thankful to the Lord for bringing us together.

Most of the guests who attended were either left-leaning or preferred to keep their opinions to themselves. I didn't want to bring anything political up and ruin their day, so I didn't talk about the story. I just let everything be about the bride and groom. Even when they asked me specifically about it, I told them just enough to get the gist across and then to respectfully wait and talk to me another day; I just needed to relax, dance, and have a couple of drinks. I knew the fallout was coming. For today, I just wanted to savor one more moment of normal.

Chapter Eleven

Unforeseen Side Effects

While I tried my best to ensure that any attacks from my interview with Project Veritas were avoided or handled immediately, there were some unfortunate side effects that I had not foreseen.

The Monday following my video release, Congressman Gosar of Arizona filed an inquiry with the U.S. Department of Health & Human Services and Indian Health Services over concerns regarding the quality of healthcare at my hospital, mentioning, "a recent interview of a nurse with Project Veritas."

I am asking that your department immediately:

1. Review all HHS health care systems nationally for compliance with vaccine reporting;
2. Inform patients if they have suffered vaccine related injuries and inform them of their right to seek compensation;
3. Remonstrate employees and contractors for not reporting;
4. Terminate employees and contractors who have deliberately jeopardized public health and harmed individual patients by not reporting vaccine-related injuries.

Thank you in advance for taking action on this and I stand by ready to discuss this with you further.

Very truly yours,

Paul A. Gosar, D.D.S.

Then, IHS (Indian Health Service) released a formal statement. What was most interesting to me about that was that they never admitted guilt or denial. Sure, they acknowledged that there was a complaint against them, but beyond that, nothing of substance.

Shortly after, my boss called me. "Jodi, I am placing you on administrative leave."

"What? Why would you do that?"

"I can't discuss that with you. We'll contact you in two weeks." And with that, she hung up. At this point, I had still not retained legal counsel. I hadn't even spoken to anyone about anything except a paralegal (at the urging of my daughter) who informed me that Arizona was a one-party consent state, and you can record without the other person knowing. Even if it wasn't legal, I still would have exposed it because of the safety issues I was seeing as a nurse. I couldn't just turn a blind eye.

I knew that becoming a whistleblower would have consequences, and I prayed long and hard before deciding to take this path. After all, I was sitting pretty with my government job and all its benefits. I made a six-figure income, chose what days I wanted to work, received a $20,000 check every year to pay off my student loans, had a pension, and was working for the Native Americans, an underserved population. I was fulfilled in all ways. However, it upset me how they were being treated by the ones who were supposed to be protecting them, and by that, I mean the removal of the advocate from the bedside, seclusion, no access to early treatment, nefarious hospital protocols and the coercion that took place with no true informed consent.

From there, things began to snowball. Next, I received a letter from the Arizona Board of Nursing stating that I had to answer multiple complaints against me. With the help of wethepatriotsusa.org, I retained counsel.

I received their first set of complaints against me in October 2021. Subsequently, the second batch of complaints was filed in November. Many of these people were anonymous, but I could tell by reading the complaints that they were a mix of my coworkers who were caught on video and their families. So naturally, they were irate to be caught on camera saying what they truly thought and felt.

One of the doctors captured on video talking with me was fired from our hospital. She was apparently a contract doctor, not a federal employee, so they just let her go. At this point, I knew enough to understand that my whistleblowing was not only upholding the ethical principles I vowed as a nurse, but it was also protected under the first amendment. This doctor was similarly protected under the first amendment and never should have been let go.

While she could have had a lawsuit against the hospital for an unlawful firing, she instead went another route in a public statement read to the board by her daughter. She filed a complaint against me with the nursing board, claiming that I was spreading "misinformation" on COVID. She also said that I was directly prescribing Ivermectin, violated HIPAA, and that I had violated her privacy by recording her. All of these claims, of course, were false.

She also said, "I'm not sure why she would want to risk her career over this. My thoughts are my own, and I got vaccinated."

Here's a lady who interjected herself into a conversation she wasn't a part of and found herself on video. As seen in the video, she was obviously passionate about her beliefs and about them not doing these studies, so why direct blame towards me when it was the federal department managing us who was breaking the law?

She had also told me on tape that she was getting tested every month to see if the natural antibodies from contracting COVID were still in her system. I'll never understand why she went through with being experimented on, having a biological agent injected into her if she already had antibodies and was tracking her immunity when she felt so strongly against it. This is yet another example of how our physicians succumbed to fear and coercion.

At this time, I also learned that the pharmacist who refused to dispence Ivermectin for COVID diagnoses had taken leave for emotional distress. She filed an injunction against me to stay away from her, claiming I had harassed and bullied her. Apparently, she was receiving messages on social media calling her names, which somehow was evidence that I was a threat to her, even when I hadn't sent nor condoned or encouraged the sending of those messages. She knew exactly what she had told me. Her words were captured on video in context. Any backlash from this was due to her words, not mine.

There was one other nurse whose name I had done my best to protect throughout all of this because she also understood what was going on. She didn't agree with all of the corruption, hospital policies that were constantly changing at the sake of the patient, nor the waste, fraud, and abuse that was occurring, and she talked about that a lot. In a video, she told me, "One day, when I'm ready to retire, I just want to blow this all up, let it all out and tell people what's been going on! You know, Jodi, there's always Project Veritas. Maybe one day we will tell them?"

I totally agree with her. All that's been going on has been terrible, and people need to know! Yet, instead of going out into the world and making real change, saving more lives, she decided to wait. She wanted to make sure she could be financially ready to retire and get her pension. There were others like her that felt the same way and would later tell me they didn't have the courage as their reason for continuing to have their pockets lined with money off of the backs of innocent people who were suffering from a corrupt medical system, before taking any kind of action. I'll never understand that train of thought, to just stand by and watch people suffer when you have the power to fight it. The problem is most people think their voice won't make a difference. I knew mine wouldn't unless it was ordained by

Yeshua.

Around the same time, as the second batch of complaints was filed with my state board of nursing, the National Council of State Boards of Nursing came out with a statement telling the country how they'd handle nurses like myself speaking out against the competing narratives. We would be punished if we stepped out of line and dared to question what the all-knowing FDA or CDC said. To me, this was especially wrong. As a nurse, I had never spoken out on anything that did not have scientific evidence to back it up and let me tell you, I had a lot of evidence on my side. I had spent more time researching COVID than getting my bachelor's and master's degrees combined. I had spent thousands of hours over the last eighteen months trying to figure out exactly what was best for my patients and society at large. And might I add that the terms misinformation and disinformation will not be found in any medical textbook. It doesn't have any role in medicine. There's simply data, scientific observation, and a multitude of opinions or interpretations. When patients see a doctor, they get opinions or second opinions. The evolution of science relies on challenging the consensus. This was laughable to me.

After being on administrative leave continuously for two months, I got another call. "Hi, Jodi, your administrative leave is over, but we're going to have to put you on investigational leave."

"Well, that's ridiculous! What am I even being investigated for?"

"You already know we can't discuss that with you, Jodi."

"What is taking so long to go through a twelve-minute video?"

This time, I had peace with their decision. I wasn't afraid of whatever would come of this investigation. I hadn't done anything wrong, let alone illegal. They were trying to find a reason to fire me, and they didn't have one. It was almost comical.

I reached out to Benjamin's school. He'd only been

attending there for about two months. I told them everything that had happened and how I was a whistleblower to Project Veritas. The school's owner said, "Listen, Jodi, we want to help you. I know somebody who can set you up with a house you can stay at so that you don't have to go to your apartment when you come back home. Whatever it is you need, we've got you."

The community response and how helpful they were amazes me. Even though many were fighting to tear me down, the vast majority still wanted to see me make it through this.

While messaging back and forth with the lady who had offered me her house to stay at, my son Benjamin started growing visibly upset. "Mom, everything's fine. You listened to what God told you to do. I don't know why we have to go hide now."

It was such a profound statement for how simple it was. Yet, he was right. I was doing exactly what God wanted me to do, and I didn't feel unsafe in our home. I felt protected there. I had gotten so caught up in the frenzy of activity surrounding me and going with the flow that I hadn't even stopped long enough to consider staying in my own home. I called her up and said, "Thank you for showing me the place, but I've been doing some thinking, and I feel safe at home. We're just going to stay here."

I was assigned an investigator through the board, who asked me various questions about the complaints, which I answered in December 2021. I also learned that the board-approved ethics evaluator was set to speak at the beginning of the meeting and present a decision tree on how the board should handle complaints of mis- and disinformation from then on. This obviously made me uneasy as I thought they would try to make a public example out of me, especially when the NCSBN (National Council of State Boards of Nursing) took their position that we should follow FDA and CDC unscientific guidelines.

We're healthcare providers. We are part of the scientific community. Scientific debate, if it's not protected, will ultimately lead to the stagnation of new technologies and the prolonged suffering of others. Evidence-based practice and scientific discourse is the only way new things are invented and old mindsets are challenged to progress forward. It entirely guides my nursing practice and is how I decide to care for and educate my patients. When researching all of this pandemic stuff like quarantining the healthy with the sick by telling everyone to stay home, the useless masks, social distancing circles telling you where to stand, and the public health implications of isolation, I based every argument on the best evidence I could find. I found that this was not the way to go, that in our vain attempts to save lives, we would only end up taking them if we continued down this path. As nurses, we took an oath to "Do No Harm." Our most important role is patient advocate.

On January 27th, 2022, I attended the Arizona Board of Nursing meeting with my family and friends in tow. I came to this meeting fired up, angry that I had to answer what I felt were baseless, unsubstantiated complaints. With the whole country afraid to take a stand for the truth, I was concerned that the board was no different. In nursing school, they drove home the idea that you never wanted to appear in front of the board. I knew going into this whole thing that it was highly political, which meant people's personal biases and ideology, if left unchecked, could easily influence the outcome just for some cheap shots against the other side.

In November, I began to sense in my spirit that I needed to find a different attorney to handle my whistleblower case with the federal government. I wanted someone just as passionate and in touch with reality as I was. Shortly after, I was led to Mike Yoder, a constitutional whistleblower attorney. His bold, unapologetic approach to all that was happening in the world at that time appealed to me. We talked for hours about my experience.

"What dollar amount are you looking for?" he asked.

"Dollar amount?" I replied. "I'm not looking for money. I want patients' rights to be protected. I want medical ethical principles to be upheld, for people to be free from coercion, and to never see the government take away individual rights in the name of a pandemic ever again."

"You know," he said. "I'm not the type of lawyer who settles."

"Good, because I'm not looking for money in my pocket. But, I do want these people to pay for what they have done."

Having Mr. Yoder as my attorney put my spirit at peace. He has a heart of a fighter and pure intentions like me, and I loved his mess-around-and-find-out approach. I told him that I had the truth on my side and the discernment to know the difference. Fast forward to this hearing in January, and at my attorneys' urging, I opted not to speak.

First, the investigator submitted her report to the Arizona Board of Nursing with the recommendation that the board order me to undergo a formal ethics evaluation and possibly even face a public decree of censure, which is the lowest form of disciplinary action that can be taken. Then, I would appear in front of the board again at their March session.

They allowed just a few minutes for my supporters to speak. One of the people who supported me that day was a recent nursing school graduate. She had reached out to me on Instagram in November 2021 as a Native American nursing student detailing the struggles she was having by refusing the shot. At that time, she was weeks away from graduation and needed to complete her final clinical rotations. However, Maricopa Community College, where she was enrolled in nursing school, told her she would be unable to graduate as she would not be allowed to complete her clinical rotations since no facility would allow her without the COVID shot.

I immediately replied to her, and we began a friendship. It

was humbling to hear that my story encouraged her to do what she felt was right. And I really felt connected to her from the outset and had deep empathy for what she was going through. Nursing school was the most stressful time of my life. It even trumped being a single teenage mom. What was happening to her and other students refusing the vaccine was just not right.

When she heard about my appearance before the board being scheduled for January, she contacted me and asked if she could speak on my behalf. She and a few others sent in character statements, which my oldest son, JJ, read before the board. Here is what Kamaleilani had to say:

"My name is Kamaleilani Moreno, and I am here today in support of Jodi O'Malley. As nurses, our main priority is the health and safety of our patients. During Jodi's time at the Phoenix Indian Medical Center, she witnessed harmful behavior and the inaction of trusted medical professionals. It is because of her bravery to speak out that these matters have been brought to light. Instead of being shamed and silenced, she should be thanked and praised. She has risked her career and her livelihood to do what is right, even though doing what is right isn't always the most popular thing to do. In my opinion, the world needs more nurses like her. I ask that you take into consideration the years that she has dedicated to walking this path, serving the general public, and taking care of those in need. She is a role model for many nurses out there and is the epitome of what we as nurses are called to do, and that is to be, above all else, an advocate for our patients. Thank you."

I felt honored to have her support. She, too, expressed that she was honored to be there for me. We had a mutual respect that made me feel like the nursing profession had some hope—that there were still some brave nurses willing to be strong. Kamaleilani represents us this way very well.

She courageously went on to sue Maricopa Community College, Arizona, won in federal court, and successfully completed nursing school. I'm told that her case has gone on to be cited as case law in other cases. But unfortunately, the media doesn't seem to have an interest in sharing that with the public.

Ultimately, the board decided to follow the investigator's recommendation, giving me forty-five days to secure an evaluator and submit an ethics evaluation.

Chapter Twelve

New Job, New Peers

Between September 2021, to January 2022, life was incredibly interesting, to say the least. After settling into my new rhythm of life, speaking, interviews, and traveling to various events around the country, some of which I was honored to be a speaker. I've appeared on many different podcasts, ranging from people with a hundred followers to those with over a million and everywhere in between. I believed the message needed to get out, and my new "job," if you will, over those months was to continue to volunteer my time to educate the populace about what was happening and encourage others to step up and do the same.

It's important to note, however, many of the tours that are dedicated to fighting back against corruption and keeping medical freedoms in the hands of the citizens often have physicians speak, but they don't invite nurses to contribute to this public conversation. This is one of the greatest missteps, in my opinion.

It's the nurses who will stand up and will stop this from happening again. Inside the hospital, we outnumber physicians by ten to one. These are the people who are willing to walk away and do what's right. Frequently, nurses will spend hours of their day helping out a patient directly. As a result, we get to know the whole person and what's happening to them mentally, physically, and spiritually. We can see what's working, both for the individual and for groups, and what isn't.

Once upon a time, nurses were the most trusted profession, except during the years of 9/11, when firefighters rightfully beat us out. But now, nobody trusts anything in the medical field. People are suspicious and can only see the greedy hospital industry that has uncanny control over a patient's medical decisions. Many people feel that they will die if they go to the hospital, so they don't go like they once did.

During the pandemic, they weren't far off on their assumption because the vast majority of COVID deaths occurred in the hospital, not at home, and not on the streets. If we nurses want to undo these perceptions, there must be a major public outcry from those willing to take a stand.

While far too many doctors and nurses remained silent, there were also many brave souls I had come to know over this time—people like Tammy Clark and Kristen Meghan. To me, they were a light in the darkness.

Since the start of the pandemic, they were my mask and PPE experts whose posts and videos I followed. You'll recall that in the hours following my Project Veritas video release, they were both reaching out to me, telling me we were family. I was floored. Before this, I was their biggest fan, and they hadn't the slightest idea of who I was, even though I had been sharing and tagging them in posts for well over a year. They provided me with such a sense of comfort and relief that not only was I not crazy, but I was following the correct science.

I looked up to them so heavily, and for so long, being accepted by them as one of them felt surreal. It was humbling to be a part of a club, Whistleblower, that is so rare.

Sometime after my disclosure went viral, I met Dr. Bryan Ardis, a chiropractor that came out of retirement to speak on the criminal hospital protocols that were killing patients. He pointed people to a 2019 study titled, *A Randomized, Controlled Trial of*

Ebola Virus Disease Therapeutics, was supported primarily by the National Institute of Allergy and Infectious Diseases (NIAID), National Institutes of Health (NIH) published in the New England Journal of Medicine. Halfway through the one-year study, the independent safety board reviewing the data pulled Remdesivir from the trial because it was found to be the only experimental drug in the trial to rate a higher than 50% (53.1% to be exact) mortality rate. It was determined to be the least effective and most deadly drug in the entire trial and was suspended. Why would Dr. Anthony Fauci lie to the world and then, in May of 2020, authorize Remdesivir (a non-FDA approved drug at that time) to be the only antiviral drug to treat all hospitalized COVID-19 Americans? I began to realize we weren't pulling dead people out of their homes or off the street. People were dying in hospitals. Why was it that the majority of deaths occurred in the hospital? I also met many wonderful doctors, some of whom had been saving, literally, thousands of lives at high personal and professional costs. These people had risked a lot and were still doing what they felt was right. Among them was Dr. Zev Zelenko, founder of the Zelenko Protocol, Dr. Peter McCullough, the founder of the McCullough Protocol, Dr. Paul Marik, Dr. Richard Urso, and Dr. Pierre Kory, founders of the FLCCC protocol, and Dr. Stella Emmanuel, to name a few. Meeting them made me more excited than I had ever been to meet somebody in my life. To be in the company of such profound, brave people was exhilarating.

In December of 2021, I asked Tammy and Kristen to meet with me at a studio to record a candid COVID conversation regarding masks and their expert opinion on their use. Dr. McCullough and Dr. Ardis also attended. We spent hours together recording. By the end, I realized that these were just amazing souls. Being in their presence with the plethora of knowledge and their willingness to travel on their own dime to educate people was incredibly inspiring.

Jodi O'Malley and Dr. Peter McCullough

Tammy and Kristen are the pathogen experts that I thought people should listen to, not Fauci and the politicians. They were the people who were in charge of our pandemic preparedness before COVID, but now they weren't on any of the decision-making committees. The people who should have been running the show were instead ostracized by a large part of the medical community, struggling to get people to listen to them.

American Frontline Industrial Hygienist and Multidisciplinary Support Summit.

Tammy and Kristen organized the American Frontline Industrial Hygienist and Multidisciplinary Support Summit. It provided all the scientific, medical, and legal information on proper pandemic response and control measures, disease mitigation strategies, real experts in the fields of exposure science and preventive medicine, and solutions for managing pandemics in the future. To learn more about them, please visit standupmichigan.com to see the five-and-a-half-hour "American Frontline Industrial Hygienist and Multidisciplinary Support Summit," broken down into three parts for easy viewing. The experts in these fields are the only professionals credentialed to lead pandemic response teams and protocols.

Interestingly, they had been blowing the whistle on the government's irresponsible and illegal response to the COVID-19 pandemic for two years. Everything we did, from the six-foot social distancing to putting masks on people and telling them to stay home—was completely against public health policies. All that any nurse or doctor had to do was sit down and Google, "What is pandemic preparedness?" or "What is a respiratory preparedness program?" and the truth would have been right in front of them.

It's insane to me how many people claimed to kneel at the altar of science, all while ignoring the people who actually knew what they were talking about. They got brainwashed into believing they were doing something good, all while shoveling money into companies who only profited off of what I consider to be a phony "vaccine."

Throughout the months following my break up with conventional medicine, there had been many ups and downs, and I've had some trouble adjusting to my new life.

I loved being a bedside nurse, the adrenaline of running to code blues, the urgency and speed my life used to have daily. Talking with patients and advocating for them was always a highlight of my week. Being able to help the most vulnerable among us without drawing much attention to myself was what my life needed. But, to say it took me some time to adjust to my newfound "fame" would be an understatement.

Not too long after that day in the studio, I went to a live medical freedom sort of event with some friends. We were supposed to be there until seven that evening. But when that time rolled around, my friends were still talking to people, having the time of their lives. I was overwhelmed.

"Hey guys, I'll be right back. I need to go get some fresh air." I excused myself as I stood up from my chair. I went outside, barely holding back the tears as I walked through the halls. I found a small curb to sit on, and I just began bawling. "God, why am I here? What more do you want me to do?"

For the past forty-seven years of my life, I'd thought I was an extrovert. After spending so much time touring the country, talking to people, and being on seemingly endless interviews, I realized I was way more introverted than I ever realized. People coming up to me, intent on building my confidence by telling me I was a hero, were instead emotionally destroying me. To this day, I don't see myself as a hero. Perhaps some of the things I did were heroic, but at the end of the day, I'm just somebody who couldn't stand back and watch humanity be destroyed from the inside out by the ones we put in power to protect us—well, everyone except Fauci. No one elected him to office.

Eventually, I began to understand the importance of the very public aspect of my new life. I realized this was where I was supposed to be. During this time, I was also especially aware of staying in constant contact with God as I had seen what fame could do to people. Many start out with genuine thoughts of good and allow the spirit of evil and its shiny strongholds to take them away from their purpose.

Chapter Thirteen

Facing The Board of Nursing

When it came time to go in front of the Arizona Board of Nursing again, I decided to speak this time. That morning, I was stressed and nervous, as anyone could imagine. I traveled to the courthouse by myself because I wanted to get there early. My kids would meet me there.

As I drove, I cranked up some worship music to get my spirit focused on the Lord's plan and prepare myself for any outcome knowing full well He is in control. I turned on Instagram live, told my followers where I was going, and asked them to sing along with me on the twenty minute drive. I just wanted to praise and worship God and share it with people. Although I couldn't see comments at the time (I was driving), I looked at the comments once I parked. A smile beamed across my face when I saw how supportive everyone was—they loved it!

On my playlist was "Nobody" by Casting Crowns, "My Jesus" by Anne Wilson, and "Different" by Micah Tyler. But the one that spoke to me and had the tears streaming down my face ruining my makeup (I didn't care) was "Less Like Me" by Zach Williams.

There is a line in Zach's song, "I still need help to see the way You see," as it played, that line opened the floodgates of tears.

"Why did you choose me, Father?" I asked. "Lord, why me?"

To know that you were chosen to expose one of the most evil things ever done to mankind all around the world is indescribable. Doing this takes incredible faith that I knew I always had. Something else I felt in my soul for years was that He was going to use me in the end times.

I remember telling that to my sister one day, and she said, "You shouldn't think that. Don't you think you will be raptured and not have to endure those times?"

I said, "I don't know how this will all work out, but I'm telling you, He led me down the path of becoming a nurse so I can help people in those times." As sure as the sun rises, I knew this. I imagined I would be used to, literally, save bodies as if in a war zone. So, in March 2020, when the whole world decided to get on board with shutting down to "slow the spread," I looked up and said to Him, "I'm supposed to pay attention to this, right?"

When I arrived, the meeting was already underway. I was incredibly nervous sitting there, waiting for my turn to come up. The good news was I already knew that my ethics evaluation came back showing I did nothing wrong and upheld the ethical principles of nursing, so the investigator struck out almost every fact that she had found in the previous report and decided to just move forward with recommending the decree of censure, which I also intended to fight. Even if there were no ramifications of this being filed other than a public slap on the wrist, I wanted others to know that when they exhibit moral courage, they will be rewarded. Using cheap intimidation tactics to pacify medical professionals will only have negative consequences for society at large.

There was a nurse practitioner whose case came up before mine. When I heard them discussing her prescribing hydroxychloroquine for COVID, my ears perked up, and I paid attention. I was relieved when the board dismissed her case. It felt good to know that they weren't politically motivated and wouldn't interfere in her patient relationship. As soon as they dismissed her, I followed her out the doors to meet in the hallway.

"Congratulations," I said as I immediately went in for a hug.

"Thank you," she smiled.

"I'm here for something similar."

"What's that?"

"I was a whistleblower regarding vaccine side effects not being reported by my hospital. I recorded some conversations and gave them to Project Veritas."

"Oh, God bless you, sister," she replied. "I will pray for a good outcome for you." Then, she asked, "Do you mind if I pray for you right now?"

So she put her hands on my shoulders, and we prayed together right then and there. This would be yet another example of Him showing up and letting me know that I was living in His will, doing exactly what He wanted me to do. That brought me so much peace. I already knew His hand was on me; no matter the decision, I would be okay.

When my name was called, it became clear that the board wanted to rule. I had the option to speak or not and decided that this time I would take a more aggressive approach and call them out. I wanted to ask them, "Why am I here? Why did I have to pay an attorney to come and answer these accusations?" Regardless of the outcome, I wanted to be sure that my voice was heard and that I was on record with why I did the things I did.

My children wanted to speak as well, and I had no idea what they were going to say. My oldest son JJ, thirty-years-old, spoke first.

"I wanted to get up here today and say a few words regarding these complaints against my mom. Typically, I am very articulate, measured, and eloquent. Today though, I find it difficult to find the words to say. Personally, I think it's absolutely appalling that freedom of speech is currently being actively censored in this country. We are seeing it play out in the media, friendships, family, social media, places of work, and now in our hospitals.

Masks don't work. The vaccinated can still spread and contract the virus. Natural immunity is stronger and more effective than the vaccine. Ivermectin is a horse drug with the Wuhan Lab leak theory. The COVID vaccines are causing blood clots, Bell's palsy, strokes, and myocarditis in otherwise normally healthy Americans. All those things were actively censored or labeled as "harmful misinformation" at the beginning of the pandemic. And many still are to this day, even though those "theories" are now proven true. My mom should be hailed as a champion of truth and an advocate for her patients. Yet here she is, having to defend herself and her career for upholding her vows as a nurse. This is pathetic and appalling, to say the least, especially since this ethics review has gone through every single complaint and found absolutely no wrongdoing. Let me repeat myself once more. NO. WRONG. DOING.

The truth will make some people uncomfortable and angry, but that doesn't make the truth a lie. We need to stop appeasing feelings when speaking about science. Science doesn't care about feelings. Science is about data that can be observed, tested, and proven. I hope that through this investigation, everyone can see that my mother broke no ethics, laws, or vows and that her actions were justified and should be commended and praised. Hopefully, this allows others out there to realize that you cannot censor the truth. We just have to be brave enough to stand up for our convictions. Thank you for allowing me to speak."

My daughter, Taylor, who is twenty-seven, went next.

"The purpose of this ethics review is to determine if there was any breach of the oath that she took as a nurse, as well as to identify whether harmful misinformation/disinformation was circulated amongst the public. Upon further review of the investigation, count by count and in extreme detail, mind you, the evaluator, whose resume and accolades speak for themselves, found my mom innocent of each complaint against her. Today we're here to deliberate if any actions need to be taken.

Personally, the actions that I believe need to be taken are, first and foremost, a public apology from IHS and from each and every one of the complainants ranging from nurses, doctors, and pharmacists, for blanketly going against the oaths they took as well as trying to publicly slander my mother's reputation and livelihood. Just to reiterate once more, no wrongdoing was found. Second, I believe IHS and the Arizona Board of Nursing are obligated to implement proper continuing education and/or a "refresher" course on healthcare transparency, the Hippocratic oath, and patient advocacy. If we're going based on the data available, then different measurements should have taken place. Lives were lost, relationships ruined, and there is an extreme distrust in the healthcare system amongst the public, regardless of which beliefs are held. At the same time, we cannot go to the past and change what has happened. However, we can take steps to ensure this doesn't happen in the future. Thank you."

Finally, my twelve-year-old son, Benjamin, spoke.

"Dear Judge.

My mom has greatly influenced my life, especially in the last few years with COVID going on. Surprisingly I wasn't scared during these tough times because my mom self-educated herself and helped me go through these times. Instead of staying home doing online school, my mom taught me self-confidence and not to be scared of what other people think. We went on adventures during COVID to other states! It was actually one of my most favorite times in my life, and my mom made it better. During my first year in middle school, one month into the year, she made the decision to pull me out to attend a new school when they introduced mandated masks. This new school was the best decision for me. At first, I didn't like it because I wanted to stay with my friends I had known since kindergarten and to play basketball for the school. But once I saw the pros and cons of both schools and got past the first stage of denial, I liked it. I have to thank my mom for that. If it wasn't for her, I'd probably not like my new school. My mom has worked very hard for everything she's got, so I'm always glad to help her when I can. During the Project Veritas video, I always tried to do the extra thing to make her happy. Before she even thought about releasing the video, she asked me for my opinion, just like she asked my siblings. She asked us, "Should I do this?" We all said, "Yes,"especially if you're feeling led to do this." I'd like to thank my mom for all that she's done for me, my siblings, and my family. Thank you for helping us get through these crazy times happily and safely."

I was in tears and so proud of them! For them to stay by my side and not succumb to the woke community and then to take a public stand on my behalf against all the propaganda was just huge. It did my mama heart good to know that I raised these amazing children. When it came to my turn, I only had a few minutes to speak. The way it works is each person gets only ten minutes to present to the board. My attorney spoke, and then my kids, so by the time they were through, my time was essentially ending. The board then granted me extra time to speak for myself. But a minute or two in, when they realized I had a prepared speech, they motioned me to wrap it up.

The evaluator noted that I had upheld my ethics and stated that no disciplinary action should be taken against me. He cited his reasons, each containing the necessary ethical principles to back me up. I was finally cleared and able to return to work (even though work wouldn't allow me to return). I wasn't sure that would ever truly be a viable option for me with all that had happened.

After that, the board discussed my case amongst themselves (right there in front of me). It was annoying to overhear them when they never once asked me questions and instead just made assumptions.

I interjected a couple of times because they were looking directly at me when they were talking, and I became defensive and said something to the effect of, "If you want to know my thoughts and feelings, then ask. Don't just sit up there and assume you know me." One board member said, "I don't think she learned her lesson, and she will do the same thing again." I kept my mouth shut this time, looking at her with a face like, "Absolutely I would if the public was in danger." Eventually, they voted, and they ruled to dismiss the case with no decree of censure. My nursing license was free of penalty and still in good standing. I won! Praise God! I was rewarded for doing the right thing!

It was such a great feeling to no longer have this hanging over my head! I thought about some of the things they discussed, like whether I had given any thought to my peers.

I empathize with those who were affected by my actions. At the same time, I can't help but feel they had the same right and ability to stick up for patients and talk about the damage being done to them, too. But I've come to realize that these were just people trying to live their lives, hoping to remain personally unaffected. They simply weren't courageous enough to research the competing narrative and to stand up and speak the truth.

The problem is, when we stick our heads in the sand, it's only a matter of time before we suffocate. The tide turns, and then we, or those we love, are affected by the continued damage this false narrative leaves in its wake.

I think so many people get caught up in, "Well, I'm just one person. What is my little story going to do?" Trust me. I felt like that, too. When I approached Project Veritas, we had already gone through a year and a half of propaganda messaging, always hearing only about all the death and decay that was supposedly surrounding us. I'd often ask myself, "What is it I'm going to show people to help them wake up? What can I possibly do?"

I think the difference is that I repeatedly asked Yeshua to use me. I understood the call, and I answered it. Seeing all of these patients being dropped off at the ER by their families, who would never see them again, leaving them to die alone in empty hospital rooms, hurt my heart. It hurt my soul. Nurses had stopped truly caring for patients just so they could limit their own exposure to COVID, and the National Emergency Act or Prep Act, instituted by Congress, allowed them liability-free ability to essentially do just that. I chose to stand up and try to do something to defend those who could not defend themselves, while many of my peers gave into the fear of losing their paychecks and peer pressure allowing the situation to overtake them.

Chapter Fourteen

What Can You Do?

There's no denying it. My testimony is a powerful one. I'm a nurse who exposed wrongdoing and had my livelihood on the line, just as many other medical professionals did. Highly esteemed physicians and experts in their field, such as Dr. Peter McCullough and Dr. Paul Merrick, also came out and have since gone under attack to educate and treat their patients. I pray that my fellow nurses, doctors, and ancillary workers will continue to stand up for our patients, do what's right, and overcome the greed and evil that continues to take rise. If enough of us band together, we can completely revitalize the landscape of our world and healthcare system and change the tyranny that's happening.

They must be stopped. Whatever the personal cost to myself, I want other nurses to use my case as a precedent so that they can come forward and bring to light the horrors they've witnessed.

In the months following my video release, everywhere I went, people kept saying to me over and over, "You are so brave. You are so courageous." But I never felt like I was brave. Doing what I did was just part of being me. I've always stood up to the bully and spent a lot of my childhood years physically fighting them.

I remember when I was pregnant, at sixteen, and people

would say, "What do you want, a boy or a girl?" Of course, most people would answer, "Well, I just want the baby to be healthy." But I would always say, "I just want my child to know who God is because if they know who God is and they have a relationship with Jesus, then they're going to be fine, no matter what." This means that if they are born with a deformity or if something tragic were to happen to them later in life, if they know and have a personal relationship with our heavenly Father, they will be fine.

You see, I was raised in a spirit-filled, Pentecostal church. Every week, we met in our small storefront church with ten pews on each side of the aisle and wood paneling on all four walls. It was in the inner city of Chicago, in a bad part of town, right next to a liquor store. Many times, drunks, prostitutes, and druggies would stagger in, in the middle of the service. Even the homeless city dwellers came in to sit in the back of the church. And sometimes, the stench would be overwhelming, but my preacher would preach and continue with service, and no one would bring attention to them.

I hadn't thought about those days in years, but after my story was released, an old memory came to mind. I was twenty years old, and I'd gone over to my preacher's home. She and her husband lived in the apartment above the church. I was distraught after leaving my husband and out on my own with my two small children, and in need of some guidance.

"Jodi," she said, "there's a calling on your life."

"What do you mean?" I asked.

"Well, over the years, there have been times when I was preaching, and I'd look out and see this light shining all around you."

It's important to know that I've never been a "Holy roller." Trust me. I have flaws, and I know exactly what they are. There are things that I sometimes indulge in, like when I've had a little too much alcohol and cigars, LOL. And I still have times when

I indulge too much in food. I just never really looked at church the way that a lot of people do. To me, it's not this place where perfect people sit together and try to become more perfect in their works and their ways of being. I never put God in a box.

No, to me, being a follower of Yeshua is all about having an intimate relationship with the Holy Spirit and glorifying God the Father to the best of my ability. And He's not shocked when I make mistakes. I'm human, after all. I do my best to recognize them, ask for forgiveness, and keep it moving.

If you have a relationship with God and ask to live in His will and not your own, there's a lot of peace that comes with it. I submit to Him, for I feel we are all here on this earth at this moment in time, for such a time as this. While walking in His will for our life doesn't take away worldly feelings such as sadness or stress, it is for His purpose and the greater good. He created me, so why would I not trust His plan? This is so important— now more than ever before. These are biblical times we are living in! I truly believe that the last days are not far ahead of us.

"But know this, that in the last days perilous times will come: For men will be lovers of themselves, lovers of money, boasters, proud, blasphemers, disobedient to parents, unthankful, unholy, unloving, unforgiving, slanderers, without self-control, brutal, despisers of good, traitors, headstrong, haughty, lovers of pleasure rather than lovers of God, having a form of godliness but denying its power. And from such people turn away!"

- 2 Timothy 3:1-5

We live in a time when most of our leaders call evil good and good evil. As a result, most of us can easily see verses one through four coming to fruition. But verse five is the one that bothers me most.

For far too many years, we've had these cookie-cutter preachers telling us that if we'll just be kind and do good works, we can live this life of abundance. It's all up to you, after all. What bunk! The prosperity gospel has taken its toll on the American church, and the confusion set out on the world by the leaders of the church is astounding. We're rapidly coming to a point where people aren't going to know what the truth is.

A study in 2021 showed that among the 176 million people who claim to be Christian, only 6% of U.S. adults possess a biblical worldview, believing the Bible to be accurate and reliable. Scarier still is the study released in 2022 showing only 37% of pastors possess a biblical worldview. The blind are officially leading the blind, and they are leading them straight to hell.

The only way we will know the truth is by knowing the Word of God and having it imprinted on our hearts so that we can discern the signs of the times we're in. Like when I looked up to heaven in March 2020 and said, "I should pay attention to this, right?" If my preacher did not preach end times prophecy, I would have never known to do that. Discernment told me to do that, and because of that, I did not fear. Instead, I had a clear mind to see what was actually taking place. Why was it that the vast majority of churches shut down for months while strip clubs and casinos were allowed to stay open? And they allowed it! I came to find out that they feared they would lose their 501(c)3 tax status if they did. This was another example of putting money over people at a time when they needed church the most.

The good news is that the Lord is calling His remnant together, those who are in love, bold, and on fire for Yeshua. I believe He is calling the church back to its original state, like the early church in the Book of Acts. It was filled with radical, revolutionary, spirit-filled, unafraid, uncompromised, and bold world changers.

When I see the dark days ahead, because they're coming, they're absolutely coming, I want to know I've done everything in my power to warn and help all I can.

We must get our priorities in order—faith and love, family, community, and friendships. But most importantly, we must submit to the authority of God, recognizing that He is in control. That's what's important.

And here's the good news, I see people all around me becoming bolder in Christ, even though the world is telling us not to. Finding a community of believers with a biblical worldview to partner with in times of trouble will become essential.

Thankfully, He has an army that He's raising to drive back the darkness and to make His name known throughout all the earth. I know because I continue to meet so many people called to the mission, many of whom are mentioned in this book.

At the end of the day, I believe that most people are genuine and want to be good, but I've come to realize just how rare courage actually is... but it doesn't have to be.

When people started asking me where I found the courage to blow the whistle on the United States federal government, I began to ask myself the same question. It was so natural to me. It seemed automatic, as if it was innate. And as I pondered that question, I came to understand on a deeper level than I'd ever understood before that I can do all things through Christ who strengthens me.

And here's the thing. So can you! The Bible says He is no respecter of persons. That means He doesn't play favorites. The same power that is available to me, through Yeshua is available to you. All you have to do is ask for forgiveness for your sins, confess your faith (the size of a mustard seed) in Yeshua, and make Him the Lord of your life. With Him by your side, you have no reason to be afraid. And the peace that comes along with that, you want that, trust me. Only the Holy Ghost can give you that kind of inner peace. I had a friend tell me the other day she feels like God is tugging on her heart, but she doesn't have the faith that I do. I told her I've been walking with the Lord for a long time, and my faith has grown, but all it takes is having faith the size of a mustard seed. Then, watch it grow! She thought she couldn't have any doubts. That is not true. I had doubts in the beginning.

I'm asked all the time, "What can people do?" I think that the most important thing that any of us can do is exhibit moral courage and raise our children in truth, love, and light, with a foundation of moral principles based on the Word of God. We must walk boldly in His truth. I think the best way to do that is to pull our children out of the public school system and teach them ourselves. I believe that these days, we have to be extremely careful who our children are learning from for six hours a day. We may be able to view the curriculum but have zero clue of the values, morals, and belief system of the one teaching it. They are impressionable, delicate little beings, and public school is indoctrination at its finest.

Now in my forties, I realize how little I learned in school, especially concerning our Constitution and our rights. We memorized for a test, but how much did we actually retain? Do you realize that the states carry more power than the federal government? I know some think that is ridiculous, but it is what saves us from an authoritarian government taking over our land, which our founding fathers had the foresight to protect us from.

And then you look at how our youth are targeted these days. We told them they could kill grandma if they didn't wear a mask. We shut down our parks and put police caution tape on the monkey bars. Then we injected them with an experimental mRNA technology with no long-term safety studies for something they have statistically zero chance of dying from, and that shot doesn't prevent sickness or transmission. If they aren't being hunted for human trafficking or influenced to become drug addicts with the Fentanyl pouring over our open borders, they are being pursued with ideologies of destruction. Many of America's children don't even know whether they are boys or girls. Our healthcare system is performing gender mutilation on pubescent children that will sterilize them forever! On top of that, there are celebrities (and teachers) pushing this brainwashing agenda, and we're just supposed to sit back and agree with it because we don't want to offend anyone? Do we send our children off to school hoping they won't succumb to this WOKE narrative? Not me!

I implore you to teach your children the important things they need to know to live a peaceful, joyous life in America, so its founding principles continue to be intact when they are old. We cannot trust many of our teachers and our schools because people are fearful of losing their paychecks, so they bow down to whatever they are told to do. Furthermore, we don't know what their private ideologies are or how much they wish to impress them on our children. Look at the number of hours your child will spend with teachers in their lifetime compared to the hours of their precious childhood spent with you. That spoke volumes to me.

I decided to homeschool my twelve-year-old because I have no faith and trust in our education system anymore. I have a duty as a parent and to the community to raise my son knowing the Constitution and our country's history—all of it—the good, the bad, and the ugly. Doing so, I've realized that they don't need all those hours in school getting indoctrinated. It only takes a few hours a day to teach them what they are expected to know at their grade level. Then, for the rest of the day, you can focus on their passions, the things God created them to do for His purposes, not to mention time for Bible, family, and fun. It's a fantastic lifestyle, far above the typical six to eight hours at school, then sports, then homework, where they are exhausted, and you are exhausted, and you only spend quality time on weekends.

It's not as hard as some may make it sound, either. When I started homeschooling, I covered the basics that my son should know. For the rest, I prayed and asked God to show me where He wanted me to start. Did He want me to do history and the Bible at the same time? Should I start with the book of Genesis? Do I begin with the Mayflower?

Like, "What do you want me to teach my son, Lord?"

I left the house shortly after that prayer, and I noticed the license plate on the car in front of me said, "NEBCNZR." I knew that Nebuchadnezzar was a king from the Bible, but I didn't know the story.

The next day, I was talking with my sister about some things that had transpired the previous night while out to dinner with Dr. McCullough. By the way, the story of his journey of faith is awe-inspiring. Hopefully, one day he will share it publicly.

As I was saying, my sister began telling me the story of Nebuchadnezzar. I couldn't believe it, there was that name again!

She said, "You know, Daniel had his three friends, Shadrack, Meshack, and Abendigo, and they were about Benjamin's age."

And I said, "What?" laughing out loud.

So, that's where we started. Benjamin and I began learning about Daniel. We watched a movie and then read the Bible and talked about it. That was really cool, you know?

Then another day, I went for a drive, and when I returned home, I pulled my truck up to where I normally park. Then, I heard the Lord whisper, "Stop. Park here." And so I stopped. But then I thought about it and said to myself, "I don't normally park here. I'm going to pull up a few feet." So I pulled up and heard, "No, Jodi. Listen. Listen." So, I rolled the truck back a few feet again and threw it in park, thinking to myself, "That was weird."

About an hour later, a big monsoon came through our town, and I heard Benjamin say, "Mom, a tree branch just fell!" I looked out the window to see what he was talking about, and there was this huge tree that broke off right where I would normally park my truck. If I didn't listen to Him, my truck would have been totaled. The maintenance guy had to use a chainsaw to cut it up just so he could move it.

Our Father wants a relationship with us, and He talks to us in the strangest of ways, but we will never get to know Him unless we trust Him. We must start actively asking for Him to talk to us and show us what He wants us to do and where He wants us to be. That includes whether and how to homeschool our children.

Please consider it. Our children are our future. If we are going to have any hope of keeping America the way we've grown to love her (prior to 2020), it is going to start with our children. We must get the message across to them about how important it is to be a critical thinker, speak truth, and how to combat the woke doctrine being pushed upon all of us.

I think Yeshua is appalled and disgusted by all that is going on in our world, especially in the body of Christ. I really believe that He will handle the church, and He will be removing people from leading it further into destruction. Those who do not walk in alignment with His teachings, those that were there for nefarious purposes, He will remove them.

I also believe that a great spiritual awakening is coming across this world. Everybody knows that there's something up. Everyone senses the evil that is taking over our nation. No matter what they believe in, they feel like things are just messed up. It's time we all realized that we are in a battle of good versus evil, you know? We're all here right now, living and breathing in what appears to be biblical times. That's powerful. All we need to do is just try to develop a relationship with Him more. We do that by talking to Him, asking Him to show us His ways, picking up the Bible and reading His Word, finding Messianic preachers and pastors like Jonathan Cahn, or listening to Discovering the Jewish Jesus, or Jack Hibbs. I love them. Finding somebody who you trust and that speaks to you can help you become more mature in the Word. Relationships take time and work. When you meet a new friend, you take the time to listen and learn who they are, and that is what draws you closer. It's the same with our relationship with our Father.

Then, you begin to hear and see Him everywhere! He starts showing up and, just like, "All right, my faithful follower, this is what I want you to do next."

Then, we just do it. We do it in kindness and love, asking Him to give us strength. It's just so powerful.

There is so much more I could say, and there will continue to be wrongs that need to be made right. My story is still unfolding, and so is yours. As we walk into the future, here is what I want you to know. The truth will always win. It will always outshine the darkness. Please, don't be like everyone else who put their heads down and continue to "go with the flow" even though they don't believe in it. The days of being silent because you don't want confrontation are over. I encourage you to speak the truth with love and kindness. Do it not because you need to change people's minds but simply because the act itself is the right thing to do.

And you don't have to do it alone.

Please continue with me in this fight. I invite you to join me and a community of believers who are taking a stand for what is right and getting bolder in Yeshua every single day. If you'd like to join us, or you need some help getting to a place of boldness, please reach out to me at www.jodiomalleyrn.com.

Remember, this world is not our home. There is power in all of us working together as one. And if we all do this, and we show others how to do this, then courage won't be so rare anymore.

Endnotes

Chapter One

Boodman, Eric. 2020. "First Covid-19 Outbreak in a U.S. Nursing Home Raises Concerns." STAT. http://facebook.com/statnews/. February 29, 2020. https://www.statnews.com/2020/02/29/new-covid-19-death-raises-concerns-about-virus-spread-in-nursing-homes/.

Feuer, Will. "First Covid-19 Outbreak in a U.S. Nursing Home Raises Concerns." CNBC.Com, CNBC, 4 Apr. 2020, https://www.statnews.com/2020/02/29/new-covid-19-death-raises-concerns-about-virus-spread-in-nursing-homes/.

"U.S. Surgeon General on Twitter: 'Seriously People- STOP BUYING MASKS!   They Are NOT Effective in Preventing General Public from Catching #Coronavirus, but If Healthcare Providers Can't Get Them to Care for Sick Patients, It Puts Them and Our Communities at Risk! Https://T.Co/UxZRwxxKL9.'" Twitter, Twitter, 29 Feb. 2020, https://web.archive.org/web/20200303020926/https://twitter.com/Surgeon_General/status/1233725785283932160.

Petty, Stephen. "Stephen Petty - On PPE and Aerosols." Youtube, YouTube, 17 Apr. 2021, https://www.youtube.com/watch?v=oYEo4T6V25w.

Chapter Two

Miller, Ryan W., and Joel Shannon. 2020. "'America's Frontline Doctors' Tout Hydroxychloroquine: Who Are They?" USA TODAY. USA TODAY. July 30, 2020. https://www.usatoday.com/story/news/nation/2020/07/30/americas-frontline-doctors-tout-hydroxychloroquine-covid-who-they/5535096002/.

Chapter Three

"AHA Letter to Surgeon General Re: Elective Surgeries and COVID-19 | AHA." 2020. American Hospital Association. March 15, 2020. https://www.aha.org/lettercomment/2020-03-15-aha-letter-surgeon-general-re-elective-surgeries-and-covid-19.

"New COVID-19 Treatments Add-On Payment (NCTAP) | CMS." 2020. Home - Centers for Medicare & Medicaid Services | CMS. Centers for Medicare & Medicaid Services . November 2, 2020. https://www.cms.gov/medicare/covid-19/new-covid-19-treatments-add-payment-nctap.

O'Malley, Jodi. 2020. "Facebook Post." Facebook. March 27, 2020. https://www.facebook.com/photo.php?fbid=10220820001159333&set=a.4483382052138&type=3.

Scarpa, Raffaele, Francesco Caso, Luisa Costa, Saverio Passavanti, Maria Grazia Vitale, Claudia Trojaniello, Antonio Del Puente, and Paolo A Ascierto. 2020. "May the Analysis of 1918 Influenza Pandemic Give Hints to Imagine the Possible Magnitude of Corona Virus Disease-2019 (COVID-19)? | Journal of Translational Medicine | Full Text." BioMed Central. Journal of Translational

Medicine. December 22, 2020. https://translational-medicine. biomedcentral.com/articles/10.1186/s12967-020-02673-6.

Chapter Four

"Emergency Use Authorization for Vaccines Explained | FDA." 2020. U.S. Food and Drug Administration. FDA. November 20, 2020. https://www.fda.gov/vaccines-blood-biologics/vaccines/ emergency-use-authorization-vaccines-explained.

Gaines, Kathleen. n.d. "What Is the Nursing Code of Ethics? | Nurse.Org." Nurse.Org. Accessed November 28, 2022. https:// nurse.org/education/nursing-code-of-ethics/.

Hinton, Denise. 2020. "Letter Revoking EUA for Chloroquine Phosphate and Hydroxychloroquine Sulfate." FDA.Gov. June 15, 2020. https://www.fda.gov/media/138945/download.

Mehr, Mandeep R, Frank Ruschitzka, and AmitN Patel. 2020. "Retraction—Hydroxychloroquine or Chloroquine with or without a Macrolide for Treatment of COVID-19: A Multinational Registry Analysis - The Lancet." The Lancet. The Lancet. June 5, 2020. https://www.thelancet.com/journals/lancet/article/ PIIS0140-6736(20)31324-6/fulltext.

Chapter Eleven

"NCSBN." 2021. NCSBN. November 16, 2021. https://www.ncsbn.org/PolicyBriefDisseminationofCOVID19Info.pdf.

Gosar, D.D.S., Paul. 2021. "Letter To Congress." Gosar. House.Gov. September 23, 2021. https://gosar.house.gov/uploadedfiles/20210923_sec._becerra_letter.pdf.

Chapter Twelve

Ardis, Bryan. n.d. "Remdesivir Research and Documents." Home. Accessed November 28, 2022. https://thedrardisshow.com/remdesivir-research-and-documents.

Chapter Fourteen

Munsil, TracyF. 2022. "New Study Shows Shocking Lack of Biblical Worldview Among American Pastors - Arizona Christian University." Arizona Christian University - Transforming Culture With Truth. Arizona Christian University. May 12, 2022. https://www.arizonachristian.edu/2022/05/12/shocking-lack-of-biblical-worldview-among-american-pastors/#:~:text=In%20fact%2C%20just%20slightly%20more,hybrid%20worldview%20known%20as%20Syncretism.

"Provisional COVID-19 Deaths by Sex and Age | Data | Centers for Disease Control and Prevention." 2022. Data | Centers for Disease Control and Prevention. Centers for Disease Control and Prevention. November 23, 2022. https://data.cdc.gov/widgets/9bhg-hcku?mobile_redirect=true.

Schneider, Rabbi. n.d. "Discovering The Jewish Jesus - With International Evangelist Rabbi K. A. Schneider." Discovering The Jewish Jesus. Accessed November 28, 2022. https://discoveringthejewishjesus.com/.

Shepherd, Josh. 2021. "Survey Finds Only 9% of Self-Identified Christians Hold to Biblical Worldview." The Roys Report. The Roys Report. September 10, 2021. https://julieroys.com/george-barna-survey-biblical-worldview/.

About the Author

Jodi O'Malley is a master's prepared critical care nurse in a federal hospital for Native Americans. Her nearly two-year experience treating COVID patients ended abruptly when she courageously shared her insider video, which went viral with over 5 million views in just a few days showing the extent of underreported vaccine injuries and outright corruption of the healthcare system where policy and protocol have taken precedence over the Patient's Bill of Rights.

Today, she continues to be a strong advocate for patient rights and for healthcare professionals to honor their oaths and ethical principles. She is also a motivational speaker who encourages others to be bold and on fire for the TRUTH.

She lives in Arizona with her thirteen-year-old son, Benjamin. Her oldest son, JJ, daughter, Taylor, and her grandson live nearby. In her spare time, she loves to travel and experience the world.

Connect with Jodi
www.jodiomalleyrn.com
Facebook: @jodi.omalley.7
Instagram: @jodiomalleyRN
TikTok: jodiomalleyMRN

Printed in the USA
CPSIA information can be obtained
at www.ICGtesting.com
LVHW040203150823
755268LV00009B/184